PRIMARY

comprehension

Fiction and nonfiction texts

Science Fiction

Poetry

Mystery

Myth/Legend

Fable

Play

Adventure

Fantasy

Fairytale

Horror/Supernatural

Humorous

Published by Prim-Ed Publishing
www.prim-ed.com

6254C

PRIMARY COMPREHENSION *(Book B)*

Published by Prim-Ed Publishing 2006
Reprinted under licence by Prim-Ed Publishing 2006
Copyright© R.I.C. Publications® 2005
ISBN 1 84654 009 7
PR–6254

Additional titles available in this series:
PRIMARY COMPREHENSION *(Book A)*
PRIMARY COMPREHENSION *(Book C)*
PRIMARY COMPREHENSION *(Book D)*
PRIMARY COMPREHENSION *(Book E)*
PRIMARY COMPREHENSION *(Book F)*
PRIMARY COMPREHENSION *(Book G)*

Internet websites

In some cases, websites or specific URLs may be recommended. While these are checked and rechecked at the time of publication, the publisher has no control over any subsequent changes which may be made to webpages. It is *strongly* recommended that the class teacher checks *all* URLs before allowing students to access them.

View all pages online

Website: www.prim-ed.com
Email: sales@prim-ed.com

PRIMARY COMPREHENSION

Foreword

Primary comprehension is a series of seven books designed to provide opportunities for pupils to read texts in a variety of fiction, poetry and nonfiction genres, to answer questions at literal, deductive and evaluative levels and to practise a variety of selected comprehension strategies.

Titles in this series include:

- *Primary Comprehension* Book A
- *Primary Comprehension* Book B
- *Primary Comprehension* Book C
- *Primary Comprehension* Book D
- *Primary Comprehension* Book E
- *Primary Comprehension* Book F
- *Primary Comprehension* Book G

Contents

TEACHERS NOTES

Twenty different texts from a variety of genres are given. These include humour, fantasy, a myth/legend, folktale, mystery, adventure, horror/supernatural, fairytale, play, fable, science fiction, poetry and informational texts/nonfiction such as a timetable, letter, report, procedure, poster, map, programme, book cover and cartoon.

Three levels of questions are used to indicate the reader's comprehension of each text.

One or more particular comprehension strategies has been chosen for practice with each text.

Each text is given over four pages. Each group of four pages consists of:

~ a teachers page

~ pupil page – 1 (which always includes the text and sometimes literal questions)

~ pupil page – 2 (which gives literal, deductive and evaluative questions)

~ pupil page – 3 (which concentrates on the chosen comprehension strategy/ strategies)

Teachers page

The **title of the text** is given.

Question types and comprehension strategies refer to the three levels of questioning and any particular strategies used.

The particular text **genre** is given.

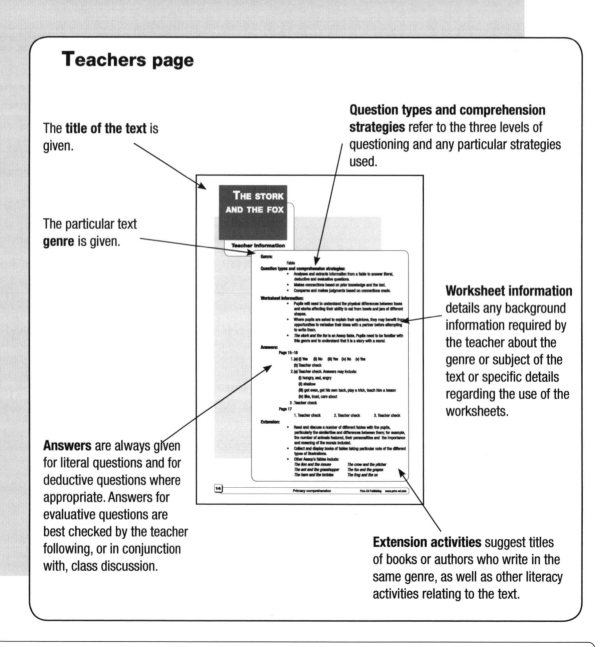

Worksheet information details any background information required by the teacher about the genre or subject of the text or specific details regarding the use of the worksheets.

Answers are always given for literal questions and for deductive questions where appropriate. Answers for evaluative questions are best checked by the teacher following, or in conjunction with, class discussion.

Extension activities suggest titles of books or authors who write in the same genre, as well as other literacy activities relating to the text.

TEACHERS NOTES

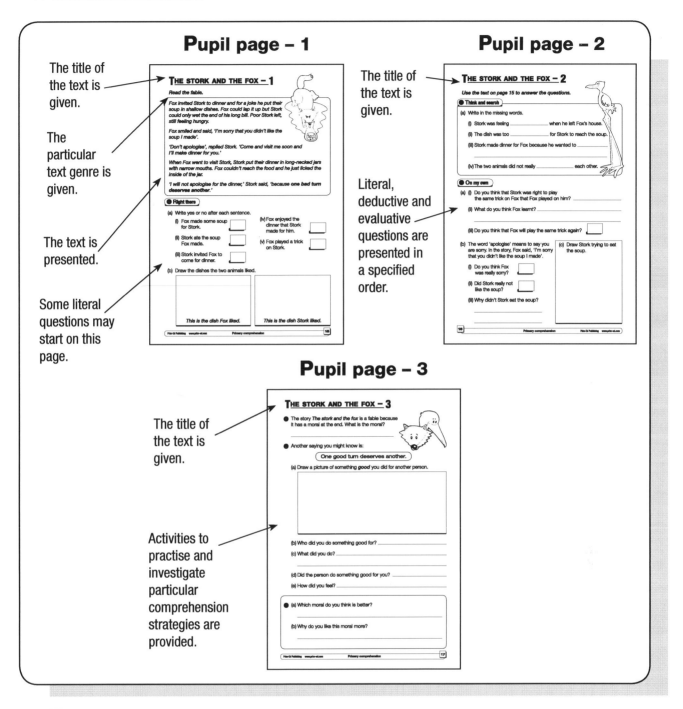

Pupil page – 1

The title of the text is given.

The particular text genre is given.

The text is presented.

Some literal questions may start on this page.

Pupil page – 2

The title of the text is given.

Literal, deductive and evaluative questions are presented in a specified order.

Pupil page – 3

The title of the text is given.

Activities to practise and investigate particular comprehension strategies are provided.

Types of questions

Pupils are given **three types (or levels) of questions** to assess their comprehension of a particular text in each genre:

- **Literal questions ('Right there')** are those which can be found directly in the text. These come first in the questions and are grouped.
- **Deductive (or inferential) questions ('Think and search')** follow the literal questions. Deductive questions are implied in the text and require the reader to read between the lines and think a bit more deeply about what has just been read.
- **Evaluative (or response/applied) questions ('On my own')** require the reader to think even further about the text and incorporate his/her personal experiences and knowledge to answer.

Answers for literal questions are always given and may be found on the teachers page. Answers for deductive questions are given where appropriate. Evaluative questions are best checked by the teacher following, or in conjunction with, class discussion.

TEACHERS NOTES

Comprehension strategies

Reading comprehension is an essential part of the reading process. Pupils need to comprehend what they read in order to become fluent readers.

The teacher is crucial in teaching and encouraging the use of comprehension strategies. Pupils' comprehension improves when teachers provide explicit instruction in comprehension strategies and when they implement activities that provide opportunities to practise and understand these strategies.

Several specific comprehension strategies have been selected for practice in this book.

Although specific examples have been selected, often other strategies, such as scanning, are used in conjunction with those indicated, even though they may not be stated. Rarely does a reader use a single strategy to comprehend a text.

Strategy definitions

Predicting

Prediction involves the pupils using illustrations, text or background knowledge to help them construct meaning. Pupils might predict what texts could be about, what could happen or how characters could act or react. Prediction may occur before, during and after reading, and can be adjusted during reading.

Pages 2–5, 6–9, 10–13, 38–41, 58–61, 66–69 and 70–73 use the strategy of predicting.

Making connections

Pupils comprehend texts by linking their prior knowledge and the new information given in the text. Pupils may make connections between the text and themselves, between the new text and other texts previously read, and between the text and the world.

Pages 14–17, 18–21, 22–25, 30–33, 34–37, 42–45, 54–57 and 58–61 use the strategy of making connections.

Comparing

This strategy is closely linked to the strategy of making connections. Pupils make comparisons by thinking more specifically about the similarities and differences between the connections being made.

Pages 14–17, 26–29, 30–33 and 34–37 use the strategy of comparing.

Sensory imaging

Sensory imaging involves pupils utilising all five senses to create mental images of passages in the text. Pupils use visual, auditory, olfactory, kinaesthetic or emotional images as well as their personal experiences to create these images. The images may help them to make predictions, form conclusions, interpret information and remember details.

Pages 34–37, 38–41, 42–45, 46–49 and 50–53 use the strategy of sensory imaging.

Determining importance

The strategy of determining importance is particularly helpful when pupils are trying to comprehend informational texts. It involves pupils determining the important theme or main idea of particular paragraphs or passages.

As pupils become effective readers, they will constantly ask themselves what is most important in a phrase, sentence, paragraph, chapter or whole text. To determine importance, pupils will need to use a variety of information, such as the purpose for reading, their knowledge of the topic, background experiences and beliefs, and understanding of the text format.

Pages 54–57 and 78–81 use the strategy of determining importance.

TEACHERS NOTES

Skimming   Skimming is the strategy of looking quickly through texts to gain a general impression or overview of the content. Readers often use this strategy to quickly assess whether a text, or part of it, will meet their purpose. Because this book deals predominantly with comprehension *after* reading, skimming has not been included as one of the major strategies.

Scanning   Scanning is the strategy of quickly locating specific details such as dates, places or names, or those parts of the text which support a particular point of view. Scanning is often used but not specifically mentioned when used in conjunction with other strategies.

Pages 6–9, 10–13, 26–29, 46–49, 58–61, 74–77 and 78–81 use the strategy of scanning.

Synthesising   Synthesising is the strategy which enables pupils to collate a range of information from a variety of sources in order to comprehend texts. Pupils recall information, order details and piece information together to make sense of the texts. Synthesising helps pupils to continually monitor their understanding of the text. Synthesising involves connecting, comparing, determining importance, posing questions and creating images.

Pages 62–65, 66–69, 70–73 and 74–77 use the strategy of synthesising.

Paraphrasing/Summarising

Summarising involves the processes of recording key ideas, main points or the most important information from a text. Summarising or paraphrasing reduces a larger piece of text to the most important details.

Pages 46–49 and 78–81 use the strategy of summarising/paraphrasing.

Shared and guided reading

Reading comprehension needs to be taught if pupils are to learn how to understand and engage with texts. The structure of comprehension lessons needs to provide direct teaching on the application of reading comprehension strategies.

Shared reading   To introduce the lesson, the teacher models reading the text, including a demonstration of how to use the comprehension strategies required by the specific unit of work. The demonstration might include:
* linking information in new text to prior knowledge
* generating mental images of parts of text
* asking 'why' questions
* pausing during reading and asking predictive questions

or any of the strategies outlined on pages vi and vii.

Guided reading   The pupils work in groups to complete the comprehension activities. The teacher works with and supports the pupils, prompting them to use different strategies to solve the questions; for example, the strategy modelled in the shared reading session should be applied to the text.

Plenary   Comprehension lessons should be concluded using a plenary session, giving the teacher and pupils the opportunity to discuss a range of issues, including:
* re-emphasis and practise of strategies
* clarification of misconceptions
* reflection and personal response
* explanation of how pupils solved particular questions
* presentation and discussion of work

TEACHERS NOTES

Genre definitions

Fiction and poetry

Science fiction
These stories include backgrounds or plots based upon possible technology or inventions, experimental medicine, life in the future, environments drastically changed, alien races, space travel, gene engineering, dimensional portals or changed scientific principles. Science fiction encourages readers to suspend some of their disbelief and examine alternate possibilities.

Horror/Supernatural
Stories of this type are those which aim to make the reader feel fear, disgust or horror. A number of horror stories have become classics. These include *Frankenstein* by Mary Shelley, *Dracula* by Bram Stoker and *Dr Jekyll and Mr Hyde* by Robert Louis Stevenson.

Mystery stories
Stories of this kind focus on suspense and the solving of a mystery. Plots of mysteries often revolve around a crime, such as murder, theft or kidnapping. The hero must solve the mystery, overcoming unusual events, threats, assaults and often unknown forces or enemies. Stories about detectives, police, private investigators, amateur sleuths, spies, thrillers and courtroom dramas usually fall into this genre.

Fables
A fable is a short story which states a moral. Fables often use talking animals or animated objects as the main characters. The interaction of the animals or animated objects reveals general truths about human nature.

Fairytales
These tales are usually about elves, dragons, hobgoblins, sprites or magical beings and are often set in the distant past. Fairytales usually begin with the phrase 'Once upon a time ...' and end with the words ' ... and they lived happily ever after'. Charms, disguises and talking animals may also appear in fairytales.

Fantasy
A fantasy may be any text or story which is removed from reality. Stories may be set in nonexistent worlds such as an elf kingdom, on another planet or in alternate versions of the known world. The characters may not be human (dragons, trolls etc.) or may be humans who interact with non-human characters.

Folktales
Stories which have been passed from one generation to the next by word of mouth rather than being written down are folktales. Folktales may include sayings, superstitions, social rituals, legends or lore about the weather, animals or plants.

Plays
Plays are specific pieces of drama, usually enacted on a stage by a number of actors dressed in make-up and appropriate costumes.

Adventure stories
Exciting events and actions feature in these stories. Character development, themes or symbolism are not as important as the actions or events in an adventure story.

Humour
Humour involves characters or events which promote laughter, pleasure or humour in the reader.

Poetry
This is a genre which utilises rhythmic patterns of language. The patterns include meter (high and low stressed syllables), syllabification (the number of syllables in each line), rhyme, alliteration, or a combination of these. Poems often use figurative language.

Myths
These are stories which explain a belief, practice or natural phenomenon and usually involve gods, demons or supernatural beings. A myth does not necessarily have a basis in fact or a natural explanation.

Legends
Legends are told as though the events were actual historical events. Legends may or may not be based on an elaborated version of an historical event. Legends are usually about human beings, although gods may intervene in some way throughout the story.

TEACHERS NOTES

Genre definitions

Nonfiction

Reports	Reports are written documents describing the findings of an individual or group. They may take the form of a newspaper report, sports or police report, or a report about an animal, person or object.
Biographies	An account of a person's life written by another person is a biography. The biography may be about the life of a celebrity or a historical figure.
Reviews	A review is a concise summary or critical evaluation of a text, event, object or phenomenon. A review may give a perspective, argument or purpose. It offers critical assessment of content, effectiveness, noteworthy features and often ends with a suggestion of audience appreciation.
Letters	These are written conversations sent from one person to another. Letters usually begin with a greeting, contain the information to be related and conclude with a farewell signed by the sender.
Procedures	Procedures are instructions which tell how to make or do something. They use clear, concise language and command verbs. A list of materials required to complete the procedure is included and the instructions are set out in easy-to-follow steps.
Diaries	A diary contains a description of daily events in a person's life.

Other **informational texts** such as **timetables** are excellent sources to teach and assess comprehension skills. Highly visual texts such as diagrams have been included because they provide the reader with other comprehension cues and are less reliant on word recognition.

Prim-Ed Publishing   www.prim-ed.com

CURRICULUM LINKS

England   Literacy Year 2

Texts

Objectives	Adam's new friend (Pages 2–5)	Lost (Pages 6–9)	The tin trunk (Pages 10–13)	The stork and the fox (Pages 14–17)	The little people (Pages 18–21)	Fruity snacks (Pages 22–25)	Sarah's timetable (Pages 26–29)	The camping trip (Pages 30–33)	Johnny Appleseed (Pages 34–37)	A visit from Planet Zog (Pages 38–41)	Holiday island (Pages 42–45)	Monkey business at the zoo (Pages 46–49)	O'Leary's leprechaun show (Pages 50–53)	A girl called Bree (Pages 54–57)	Captain Fishhook and the buried treasure (Pages 58–61)	The honeybee's sting (Pages 62–65)	The magic trick (Pages 66–69)	The princess and the pea (Pages 70–73)	Stranded! (Pages 74–77)	The polar bear (Pages 78–81)
Term 1																				
• **Read a range of fiction and poetry:**																				
– stories with familiar settings	●		●	●				●		●							●		●	
• **Read a range of nonfiction:**																				
– instructions					●															
• **Text level work:**																				
– be aware of difference between spoken and written language	●																			
– understand time and sequential relationship in stories	●																			
– identify reasons for events in stories	●									●							●		●	
– link story themes to own experiences				●				●		●									●	
– use story structure to write in similar form			●														●			
– read simple written instructions (recipes)					●															
– use models from reading to organise instructions sequentially					●															
Term 2																				
• **Read a range of fiction and poetry:**																				
– traditional stories				●														●		
– stories from other cultures									●							●				
– poems with predictable and patterned language		●																		
• **Text level work:**																				
– discuss story themes				●																
– predict story endings/incidents		●						●								●	●			
– discuss story settings to locate key words and phrases in text								●												
– identify and describe characters				●												●	●			
– re-tell stories																●	●			
– identify patterns in poems		●																		
Term 3																				
• **Read a range of fiction and poetry:**																				
– humorous stories and verse												●	●							
• **Read a range of nonfiction:**																				
– non-chronological reports																				●

CURRICULUM LINKS

England   Literacy Year 2

Texts

Objectives		Adam's new friend (2–5)	Lost (6–9)	The tin trunk (10–13)	The stork and the fox (14–17)	The little people (18–21)	Fruity snacks (22–25)	Sarah's timetable (26–29)	The camping trip (30–33)	Johnny Appleseed (34–37)	A visit from Planet Zog (38–41)	Holiday island (42–45)	Monkey business at the zoo (46–49)	O'Leary's leprechaun show (50–53)	A girl called Bree (54–57)	Captain Fishhook and the buried treasure (58–61)	The honeybee's sting (62–65)	The magic trick (66–69)	The princess and the pea (70–73)	Stranded! (74–77)	The polar bear (78–81)
Term 3	**Text level work:**																				
	– read humorous stories and poems and respond imaginatively												●		●						
	– discuss meanings of words/phrases that create humour in poetry														●						
	– write sustained stories												●								
	– use humorous verse as a structure for children to write their own by adaptation														●						
	– scan a text to find specific sections							●				●		●		●					●
	– speculate what a book might be about															●					
	– make simple notes from nonfiction texts																				●
	– write nonfiction texts, using texts read as models for own writing									●											

Northern Ireland   English (Reading) Year 3

		Adam's new friend	Lost	The tin trunk	The stork and the fox	The little people	Fruity snacks	Sarah's timetable	The camping trip	Johnny Appleseed	A visit from Planet Zog	Holiday island	Monkey business at the zoo	O'Leary's leprechaun show	A girl called Bree	Captain Fishhook...	The honeybee's sting	The magic trick	The princess and the pea	Stranded!	The polar bear
Range	• engage with a range of texts, including:																				
	– stories	●			●	●			●	●		●					●	●	●	●	
	– poems		●												●						
	– plays			●																	
	– informational materials						●	●				●		●		●					●
	– environmental print							●						●							
	– visual materials	●											●	●		●					
Purpose	• read for information	●	●	●	●	●	●	●	●	●	●	●	●	●	●	●	●	●	●	●	●
Reading activities	• take part in shared reading experiences	●	●	●	●	●	●	●	●	●	●	●	●	●	●	●	●	●	●	●	●
	• retell/reread poems or stories	●				●											●	●	●		
	• make use of environmental print			●			●	●						●							
Expected outcomes	• begin to use evidence from the text to support their views	●	●	●	●	●	●	●	●	●	●	●	●	●	●	●	●	●	●	●	●
	• show understanding of ways texts are structured by representing ideas through pictures and diagrams		●	●				●		●		●	●	●		●	●	●	●		
	• collect information relevant to specific purposes and represent their findings in a variety of ways	●	●	●	●	●	●	●	●	●	●	●	●	●	●	●	●	●	●	●	●
	• read a wide range of texts independently and discuss what has been read	●	●	●	●	●	●	●	●	●	●	●	●	●	●	●	●	●	●	●	●

CURRICULUM LINKS

Republic of Ireland
English Language (Reading)
1st Class

Texts

Objectives		Adam's new friend (Pages 2–5)	Lost (Pages 6–9)	The tin trunk (Pages 10–13)	The stork and the fox (Pages 14–17)	The little people (Pages 18–21)	Fruity snacks (Pages 22–25)	Sarah's timetable (Pages 26–29)	The camping trip (Pages 30–33)	Johnny Appleseed (Pages 34–37)	A visit from Planet Zog (Pages 38–41)	Holiday island (Pages 42–45)	Monkey business at the zoo (Pages 46–49)	O'Leary's leprechaun show (Pages 50–53)	A girl called Bree (Pages 54–57)	Captain Fishhook and the buried treasure (Pages 58–61)	The honeybee's sting (Pages 62–65)	The magic trick (Pages 66–69)	The princess and the pea (Pages 70–73)	Stranded! (Pages 74–77)	The polar bear (Pages 78–81)
Receptiveness to language	• experience the reading process being modelled	●	●	●	●	●	●	●	●	●	●	●	●	●	●	●	●	●	●	●	●
	• engage in shared reading activities	●	●	●	●	●	●	●	●	●	●	●	●	●	●	●	●	●	●	●	●
	• develop reading skills through engaging with reading materials appropriate to his/her stage of development	●	●	●	●	●	●	●	●	●	●	●	●	●	●	●	●	●	●	●	●
	• adapt his/her reading style for different purposes	●	●	●	●	●	●	●	●	●	●	●	●	●	●	●	●	●	●	●	●
Competence and confidence	• perform simple information retrieval tasks	●	●	●	●	●	●	●	●	●	●	●	●	●	●	●	●	●	●	●	●
Developing cognitive abilities	• develop comprehension strategies	●	●	●	●	●	●	●	●	●	●	●	●	●	●	●	●	●	●	●	●
	• predict future events and outcomes in a story	●	●	●							●		●				●	●	●		
Emotional and imaginative development	• engage with a wide variety of text	●	●	●	●	●	●	●	●	●	●	●	●	●	●	●	●	●	●	●	●
	• respond to characters and events in a story		●	●	●				●	●		●					●	●	●	●	
	• explore different attitudes and feelings by imagining what it would be like to be certain characters	●			●						●	●	●						●	●	

Scotland   English Language (Reading)   Primary 3

Level A																					
Level A	• **Reading for information:**																				
	– develop confidence in handling information	●	●	●	●	●	●	●	●	●	●	●	●	●	●	●	●	●	●	●	●
	– answer questions	●	●	●	●	●	●	●	●	●	●	●	●	●	●	●	●	●	●	●	●
	• **Reading for enjoyment:**																				
	– experience wide range of story and informational texts	●	●	●	●	●	●	●	●	●	●	●	●	●	●	●	●	●	●	●	●
	– teacher models good reading habits	●	●	●	●	●	●	●	●	●	●	●	●	●	●	●	●	●	●	●	●
	• **Reading to reflect on the writer's ideas and craft:**																				
	– discuss texts and answer questions	●	●	●	●	●	●	●	●	●	●	●	●	●	●	●	●	●	●	●	●
	– predict what might happen next	●	●	●							●		●				●	●	●		
	– pick out important ideas in a text	●	●	●	●	●	●	●	●	●	●	●	●	●	●	●	●	●	●	●	●
	• **Awareness of genre:**																				
	– look at covers, illustrations and titles															●					
Level B	• **Reading for information:**																				
	– look at printed environmental text						●	●				●		●							
	– look at texts with practical purpose						●	●	●			●		●		●					●
	– use wide selection of informational text						●	●	●			●		●							●

CURRICULUM LINKS

Scotland
English Language (Reading)
Primary 3

Objectives		Adam's new friend (Pages 2–5)	Lost (Pages 6–9)	The tin trunk (Pages 10–13)	The stork and the fox (Pages 14–17)	The little people (Pages 18–21)	Fruity snacks (Pages 22–25)	Sarah's timetable (Pages 26–29)	The camping trip (Pages 30–33)	Johnny Appleseed (Pages 34–37)	A visit from Planet Zog (Pages 38–41)	Holiday island (Pages 42–45)	Monkey business at the zoo (Pages 46–49)	O'Leary's leprechaun show (Pages 50–53)	A girl called Bree (Pages 54–57)	Captain Fishhook and the buried treasure (Pages 58–61)	The honeybee's sting (Pages 62–65)	The magic trick (Pages 66–69)	The princess and the pea (Pages 70–73)	Stranded! (Pages 74–77)	The polar bear (Pages 78–81)
Level B	**• Reading for enjoyment:**																				
	– experience fiction and poems with a variety of styles	●	●	●	●	●					●	●		●		●		●	●	●	●
	• Reading to reflect on the writer's ideas and craft:																				
	– predict events	●	●	●							●			●			●	●	●		
	– answer questions	●	●	●	●	●	●	●	●	●	●	●	●	●	●	●	●	●	●	●	●
	– recall and refer to own experiences		●		●	●		●	●		●		●	●	●				●	●	
	– sequence thoughts and ideas	●		●			●	●									●	●	●		
	– respond through drawings and diagrams		●	●	●	●	●	●	●	●	●	●	●	●		●	●	●	●	●	●
	• Awareness of genre:																				
	– predict the nature and content of a text															●					
	• Knowledge about language:																				
	– be familiar with terms author and title															●					
	– discuss characters and scenes in fiction	●	●	●	●					●	●		●		●			●	●	●	●
	– encounter poems		●											●							
Level C	**• Reading for information:**																				
	– scan for specific information	●	●	●	●	●	●	●	●	●	●	●	●	●	●	●	●	●	●	●	●
	– identify the sequence of information in texts	●			●	●											●	●	●		
	– record information in different ways	●	●	●	●	●	●	●	●	●	●	●	●	●	●	●	●	●	●	●	
	• Reading for enjoyment:																				
	– identify with characters and comment on their behaviour and reasons		●	●	●				●				●				●	●	●	●	
	• Reading to reflect on the writer's ideas and craft:																				
	– make predictions	●	●	●							●			●			●	●	●		
	– identify ideas	●	●	●	●	●	●	●	●	●	●	●	●	●	●	●	●	●	●	●	●
	– skim and scan to verify decisions	●	●	●	●	●	●	●	●	●	●	●	●	●	●	●	●	●	●	●	●
	– go beyond literal answers to make inferences and conclusions	●	●	●	●	●	●	●	●	●	●	●	●	●	●	●	●	●	●	●	●
	• Awareness of genre:																				
	– adjust reading approaches to the different ways information is presented in different nonfiction texts									●	●	●		●		●					

CURRICULUM LINKS

Wales
English (Reading)
Year 2

Texts

Objectives

Objectives		Adam's new friend (Pages 2–5)	Lost (Pages 6–9)	The tin trunk (Pages 10–13)	The stork and the fox (Pages 14–17)	The little people (Pages 18–21)	Fruity snacks (Pages 22–25)	Sarah's timetable (Pages 26–29)	The camping trip (Pages 30–33)	Johnny Appleseed (Pages 34–37)	A visit from Planet Zog (Pages 38–41)	Holiday island (Pages 42–45)	Monkey business at the zoo (Pages 46–49)	O'Leary's leprechaun show (Pages 50–53)	A girl called Bree (Pages 54–57)	Captain Fishhook and the buried treasure (Pages 58–61)	The honeybee's sting (Pages 62–65)	The magic trick (Pages 66–69)	The princess and the pea (Pages 70–73)	Stranded! (Pages 74–77)	The polar bear (Pages 78–81)
Range	• Materials read should include these features:																				
	– interesting subject matter and settings related to own experience or beyond everyday experience	●	●	●	●	●	●	●	●	●	●	●	●	●	●		●	●	●	●	●
	– language with recognisable repetitive patterns, rhyme and rhythm		●											●							
	– straightforward characterisation and plot	●	●	●	●	●			●	●	●		●		●		●	●	●	●	
	– use of a variety of organisational and presentational techniques	●		●				●	●			●		●							●
	– illustrations that are visually stimulating and enhance the words of the text	●										●									
	• Literature read should cover the following categories:																				
	– plays			●																	
	– poems		●											●							
	– stories with familiar settings	●							●	●			●					●		●	
	– stories based on imaginary or fantasy worlds				●							●									
	– traditional folk and fairy stories				●					●							●		●		
	– stories/poems containing patterned and predictable language		●																		
	• Understand and respond to stories and poems, and in particular to:																				
	– talk about characters and events	●	●	●	●				●	●	●		●		●		●	●	●	●	
	– say what might happen next in a story	●	●	●							●		●				●	●	●		
	– retell stories	●															●	●	●		
	– read complete short texts, including playscripts	●	●	●	●	●	●	●	●	●	●	●	●	●	●	●	●	●	●	●	●
Skills	• Use reference materials						●	●				●	●		●						●

ADAM'S NEW FRIEND

Teacher information

Genre:

Cartoon

Question types and comprehension strategies:

- Analyses and extracts information from a cartoon to answer literal, deductive and evaluative questions.
- Makes predictions based on a visual text.

Worksheet information:

Pupils could discuss in pairs or as a whole class what is happening in each picture of the cartoon on page 5 and what the boy might be thinking, before completing the activity individually.

Answers:

Page 4

1. (a) Amy and Adam

   (b) They got their kites for a birthday present.

   (c) 1 The children were given kites as a present.

       2 They flew their kites at the park.

       3 The wind became stronger.

       4 The wind lifted Adam into the air.

       5 Adam landed in a tree.

       6 A bird was looking at Adam.

2. Because she had pulled her kite in.

3. Teacher check

Page 5

Teacher check

Extension:

- Pupils can cut out pictures of cartoon characters from magazines and glue them onto large sheets of paper. They can then draw speech balloons and write what they think the characters could be saying to each other.
- Pupils work in a group or pairs to create a cartoon about characters they know (e.g. a pet, family) or humorous things they have seen or had happen to them.
- Cut up simple cartoons or picture stories for pupils to sequence correctly.

ADAM'S NEW FRIEND – 1

Look at and read the cartoon.

ADAM'S NEW FRIEND – 2

Use the cartoon on page 3 to answer the questions.

❶ Right there

(a) What are the children's names? _____

(b) How did they get their kites? _____

_____

(c) Write the numbers 1 to 6 next to each sentence to show the order
of what happened in the cartoon.

☐ The wind became
stronger.

☐ A bird was looking at
Adam.

☐ They flew their kites
at the park.

☐ The children were given
kites as a present.

☐ The wind lifted Adam into
the air.

☐ Adam landed in a tree.

❷ Think and search

Why didn't Amy take off in the wind?_____

_____

❸ On my own

Imagine that the
bird and Adam talk
to each other in the
tree. In the speech
balloons, write
what you think they
would say.

ADAM'S NEW FRIEND – 3

Look at the pictures in the cartoon below. In the speech balloons, write what you think the boy might be saying to himself.

LOST

Teacher information

Genre:

Mystery (rhyme)

Question types and comprehension strategies:

- Analyses and extracts information from a mystery rhyme to answer literal, deductive and evaluative questions.
- Makes predictions based on the text and background information.
- Scans text to locate information.

Worksheet information:

- Before reading the mystery rhyme with the class, discuss some of the things that dogs do with their bones and some possible reasons why they do them.
- After reading the rhyme discuss why it is a mystery.
- Pupils may enjoy taking turns to read verses of the rhyme, adding appropriate actions. The whole class, or some of the pupils who find reading a challenge, could read the repeated verse.

Answers:

Pages 7–8

1. (a) iii   (b) i   (c) iv   (d) iii
   (e) Pupils may choose from near the back fence, in the bin, by his kennel or by the door.
2. (a) Teacher check   (b) Teacher check
3. (a) Teacher check   (b) Teacher check

Page 9

Teacher check

Extension:

- Find pairs of rhyming words in the poem and make lists of other words that also rhyme with them.
- Decide 'what is lost' and 'who lost it' then work with the class to compose a text innovation based on the repeated rhyme.

  For example:

  Where did I leave her?

  Where can she be?

  Do lots of mother cats

  Forget like me?

Lost – 1

Read the mystery rhyme.

Where did I hide it?
Where can it be?
Do lots of other puppies
Forget like me?

Is it near the back fence?
Did I hide it in the bin?
I'll have to find it soon,
Or I'll be looking thin.

Where did I hide it?
Where can it be?
Do lots of other puppies
Forget like me?

Did I put it by my kennel?
Did I leave it by the door?
If I don't find it soon,
I'll have to call the law.

Where did I hide it?
Where can it be?
Do lots of other puppies
Forget like me?

I really want to find it.
It's a very special bone.
If you won't help me find it,
I'll do it on my own.

❶ Right there

Colour the right one.

(a) The bone is …

    (i) in the bin.

    (ii) by the kennel.

    (iii) lost.

    (iv) by the door.

(b) The puppy …

    (i) looked near the door.

    (ii) put the bone near the fence.

    (iii) doesn't want any help.

    (iv) looked under the car.

(c) If he doesn't find the bone he will …

    (i) cry.

    (ii) look in his kennel.

    (iii) look by the door.

    (iv) look thin.

(d) He will call the law if he …

    (i) finds the bone.

    (ii) gets another bone.

    (iii) can't find the bone.

    (iv) wants a drink.

LOST – 2

Use the text on page 7 to answer the questions.

(e) Write the names of and draw two places the puppy looked for his bone.

[ ] [ ]

❷ Think and search

(a) Do you think the puppy will find his bone? _____

(b) Do you think that all puppies are forgetful? _____

❸ On my own

(a) Where do you think he hid his bone? Write the names of and draw two more places the puppy could look.

[ ] [ ]

(b) Tick the one where you think he will find it.

LOST – 3

1 What is something special you have that you wouldn't like someone to take?

_____

_____

2 Where do you keep it now? _____

3 If you really wanted to hide it so that no-one would find it, where could you put it? Draw your special thing in a really good hiding place.

4 Draw some of the things you have lost and the places where you found them.

Teacher information

Genre:

Play

Question types and comprehension strategies:

- Analyses and extracts information from a play to answer literal, deductive and evaluative questions.
- Makes predictions to determine possible past and future events.
- Scans text to locate words with the opposite meaning to those given.

Worksheet information:

- Pupils should be familiar with the stories of *Jack and the beanstalk* and *Aladdin and the wonderful lamp* in order to understand the references in the play.
- Opportunities to discuss possible ways of opening the trunk would be helpful to pupils before they attempt to answer Question 3 on page 12
- Page 13 requires the pupils to illustrate the possible contents of the trunk and to determine an explanation about how they came to be there. They need to understand that there is no correct answer and that they must use their imagination, together with information from the play, to make up a good story.

Answers:

Page 12

    1.   (a) (i) down (ii) full (iii) open (iv) old

           (b) (i) Yes   (ii) No   (iii) No   (iv) No   (v) Yes

    2.   Teacher check

    3.   Teacher check

Page 13

    1.   Teacher check

    2.   Teacher check

Extension:

- Dramatise individual pupil's stories about how the trunk came to be buried or what happened after it was opened.
- Discuss being scared and the types of situations or events that they find scary.

THE TIN TRUNK – 1

Read the play.

Storyteller: The children were staying at an old beach cottage. They were digging in the sand around some rocks at the side of the shed.

Tony: Hey, there is something down here, come and help me dig it out.

Shannon: Perhaps it's buried treasure! I'll get my spade and help you.

Taj: It looks really old and it's made out of metal. It's some kind of trunk.

Tari: It could be magic. Perhaps there's a genie in it who can grant us three wishes.

Tony: What an imagination! You read too many books, Tari.

Shannon: Well, what do you think is in it?

Tony: Probably some old fishing gear. Let's open it and find out.

Tari: I'm scared. There might be some magic beans in it and we can plant them and all climb up the beanstalk.

Taj: Yes, Tari, and find a hen that lays golden eggs, of course. Why don't we just go and ask Mum?

Shannon: That would be a waste of time. She's reading and she won't even listen to us when she's got her nose in a book.

Tari: Aunty Sue, Aunty Sue, I'm scared, I'm scared.

Mum: What's the matter this time, Tari?

Sam: It's OK, Mum, we've found an old trunk and she thinks there is something magic in it.

Mum: I've never seen that before. Why don't you open it up and see?

Shannon: I hope there is lots of money in it.

Sam: It's probably full of old photos or toys and things but it has a really strange lock on it which we can't get open.

Taj: I guess we'll just have to wait until Dad gets home from fishing. I wonder what we'll find.

THE TIN TRUNK – 2

Use the text on page 11 to answer the questions.

❶ Right there

(a) Find a word in the play that means the opposite of each word.

(i) up _____

(ii) empty _____

(iii) shut _____

(iv) new _____

(b) Write yes or no after each sentence.

(i) Shannon used a spade to dig out the trunk. ☐

(ii) Mum had seen the trunk before. ☐

(iii) Tari wanted them to open the trunk. ☐

(iv) Mum told them not to open the trunk. ☐

(v) The lock was hard to open. ☐

❷ Think and search

(a) Which child do you think is the youngest?

_____

(b) What does this child do to make you think this?

_____

_____

_____

_____

❸ On my own

(a) Do you think Dad will be able to open the trunk?

_____

(b) Draw Dad getting the trunk open.

THE TIN TRUNK – 3

Use the text on page 11 to complete these activities.

1 Draw a picture of what you think might be in the trunk.

2 Make up a story about how the trunk was left in the sand and write or draw the information on the chart.

Who left the trunk?	When was it left there?

Why was it left?	What did the person who left it hope would happen?

Genre:

Fable

Question types and comprehension strategies:

- Analyses and extracts information from a fable to answer literal, deductive and evaluative questions.
- Makes connections based on prior knowledge and the text.
- Compares and makes judgments based on connections made.

Worksheet information:

- Pupils will need to understand the physical differences between foxes and storks affecting their ability to eat from bowls and jars of different shapes.
- Where pupils are asked to explain their opinions, they may benefit from opportunities to verbalise their ideas with a partner before attempting to write them.
- *The stork and the fox* is an Aesop fable. Pupils need to be familiar with this genre and to understand that it is a story with a moral.

Answers:

Pages 15–16

1. (a) (i) Yes   (ii) No   (iii) Yes   (iv) No   (v) Yes

  (b) Teacher check

2. (a) Teacher check. Answers may include:

  (i) hungry, sad, angry

  (ii) shallow

  (iii) get even, get his own back, play a trick, teach him a lesson

  (iv) like, trust, care about

3. Teacher check

Page 17

1. Teacher check   2. Teacher check   3. Teacher check

Extension:

- Read and discuss a number of different fables with the pupils, particularly the similarities and differences between them; for example, the number of animals featured, their personalities and the importance and meaning of the morals included.
- Collect and display books of fables taking particular note of the different types of illustrations.
- Other Aesop's fables include:

  The lion and the mouse   *The crow and the pitcher*

  The ant and the grasshopper   *The fox and the grapes*

  The hare and the tortoise   *The frog and the ox*

THE STORK AND THE FOX – 1

Read the fable.

Fox invited Stork to dinner and for a joke he put their soup in shallow dishes. Fox could lap it up but Stork could only wet the end of his long bill. Poor Stork left, still feeling hungry.

Fox smiled and said, 'I'm sorry that you didn't like the soup I made'.

'Don't apologise', replied Stork. 'Come and visit me soon and I'll make dinner for you.'

When Fox went to visit Stork, Stork put their dinner in long-necked jars with narrow mouths. Fox couldn't reach the food and he just licked the inside of the jar.

'I will not apologise for the dinner,' Stork said, 'because **one bad turn deserves another**.'

❶ Right there

(a) Write yes or no after each sentence.

   (i) Fox made some soup for Stork. ☐

   (ii) Stork ate the soup Fox made. ☐

   (iii) Stork invited Fox to come for dinner. ☐

   (iv) Fox enjoyed the dinner that Stork made for him. ☐

   (v) Fox played a trick on Stork. ☐

(b) Draw the dishes the two animals liked.

This is the dish Fox liked.	*This is the dish Stork liked.*

THE STORK AND THE FOX – 2

Use the text on page 15 to answer the questions.

❷ Think and search

(a) Write in the missing words.

    (i) Stork was feeling _____ when he left Fox's house.

    (ii) The dish was too _____ for Stork to reach the soup.

    (iii) Stork made dinner for Fox because he wanted to _____

    _____

    (iv) The two animals did not really _____ each other.

❸ On my own

(a) (i) Do you think that Stork was right to play
       the same trick on Fox that Fox played on him? _____

    (ii) What do you think Fox learnt? _____

    _____

    (iii) Do you think that Fox will play the same trick again? ☐

(b) The word 'apologise' means to say you
are sorry. In the story, Fox said, 'I'm sorry
that you didn't like the soup I made'.

    (i) Do you think Fox
       was really sorry? ☐

    (ii) Did Stork really not
        like the soup? ☐

    (iii) Why didn't Stork eat the soup?

    _____

    _____

(c) Draw Stork trying to eat
the soup.

THE STORK AND THE FOX – 3

1 The story *The stork and the fox* is a fable because it has a moral at the end. What is the moral?

_____

2 Another saying you might know is:

> One good turn deserves another.

(a) Draw a picture of something **good** you did for another person.

(b) Who did you do something good for? _____

(c) What did you do? _____

_____

(d) Did the person do something good for you? _____

(e) How did you feel? _____

3 (a) Which moral do you think is better?

_____

(b) Why do you like this moral more?

_____

THE LITTLE PEOPLE

Teacher information

Genre:

Fantasy

Question types and comprehension strategies:

- Analyses and extracts information from a fantasy to answer literal, deductive and evaluative questions.
- Makes connections between prior knowledge and the information presented in the text.

Worksheet information:

- Before completing pages 19–20, pupils will benefit from some class discussion about why children would want to help the little people. Discussion could focus on the needs and worthiness of the little people and the attitude, knowledge and nature of children. Possible ways of helping could be discussed in small groups.
- Pupils should be aware that posters need to be attractive, give a clear, concise message and be persuasive. Pupils may like to copy their poster ideas from page 21 onto larger sheets or work with a partner to produce a large poster for display.
- Page 21 requires the pupils to list reasons for cutting down trees. Before completing the exercise, discuss the different uses of timber and land clearing for agricultural purposes.

Answers:

Pages 19–20

1. (a) (i) Yes (ii) No (iii) Yes (iv) No (v) Yes
2. Teacher check
3. Teacher check

Page 21

1. Teacher check
2. Teacher check

Extension:

- Create a collage of a forest with different types of trees and the animals which live there.
- Read and discuss stories about goblins, elves and fairies and list some of the good things they did.
  For example:
  The elves and the shoemaker   *Cinderella*
  Sleeping Beauty

THE LITTLE PEOPLE – 1

Read the fantasy.

Deep, deep in the forest the little people live. They have lived there for hundreds of years, but very few humans have ever seen them because they run away and hide whenever they hear a noise. They are kind, gentle people who work hard and enjoy the peace and quiet of the dark forest.

Today, the goblins, elves and fairies are having a meeting to discuss a terrible problem. Humans are cutting down all the trees. Even the toadstools they live in are being squashed by people and their machines. It's often so windy without the trees, that the fairies find it hard to fly.

'I'm sure that they don't want to hurt us,' said one of the younger fairies, 'but they just don't understand that soon we'll have nowhere to live'.

'They don't know about all the things we do to help them', explained an older goblin. 'Most of them don't even believe that we are real.'

'There are some children who know about us,' one of the elves added, 'because they read about us in their storybooks. Let's see if they will help us'.

'Yes, that's a great idea. We'll tell them about our problems and they will try to stop people cutting down all the trees. Anyway, I'm sure that they love the forests and will want to protect them for their own children to enjoy.'

❶ Right there

(a) Write yes or no after each sentence.

   (i) The little people run away when they hear a noise.   _____

   (ii) Fairies enjoy flying when it's windy.   _____

   (iii) The little people are worried.   _____

   (iv) People want to destroy the fairies, elves and goblins.   _____

   (v) The little people are going to ask the
       children to help them save the trees.   _____

THE LITTLE PEOPLE – 2

Use the text on page 19 to answer the questions.

② Think and search

(a) Do you think the children will want to help the

little people? _____

(b) Give two reasons.

③ On my own

(a) Would you like to help them? _____

(b) Draw how you and your friends could help the little people.

THE LITTLE PEOPLE – 3

1 Make a poster to tell people that they should not cut down too many trees. Your poster needs to be bright and colourful.

2 What are some reasons people cut down trees?
Make a list, then draw the most important reason.

- _____
- _____
- _____
- _____

FRUITY SNACKS

Teacher information

Genre:

Procedure

Question types and comprehension strategies:

- Analyses and extracts information from a procedure to answer literal, deductive and evaluative questions.
- Makes connections between text and personal experience.

Worksheet information:

Hold a class discussion to list other possible fruits and toppings that could be used for the activity on page 25, before pupils complete the activity independently

Answers:

Pages 23–24

1. (a) (i) Yes   (ii) No   (iii) No   (iv) Yes   (v) Yes

   (b) (1) Wash the fruit and pat dry with the paper towels.

     (2) Peel and cut the kiwifruit, banana and watermelon into chunks.

     (3) Carefully thread one piece of each fruit onto a skewer.

     (4) Keep going until the fruit is used up.

     (5) Put some yoghurt in a small bowl.

     (6) Add a teaspoon of yoghurt onto the skewer and eat!

2. (a) strawberry – red, kiwifruit – green, banana – yellow, grape – green, watermelon – red

   (b) The pattern would be red, green, yellow, red, red instead of red, green yellow, green, red.

3. Teacher check

Page 25

Teacher check

Extension:

- Pupils may enjoy reading (and making!) simple recipes in children's cookbooks. Some suitable titles are:

The healthy body cookbook: Over 50 fun activities and delicious recipes for kids by Joan D'Amico and Karen Eich Drummond

Better homes and gardens new junior cookbook by Jennifer Dorland Darling

Pretend soup and other real recipes by Mollie Katzen and Ann Henderson

A first cookbook for children by Evelyne Johnson

Betty Crocker's kids cook by Betty Crocker

FRUITY SNACKS – 1

Read the procedure.

You will need:

- strawberries, kiwifruit, banana, green grapes, watermelon
- tub of strawberry yoghurt
- cutting board
- blunt knife
- paper towels
- small bowl
- teaspoon
- wooden skewers with the sharp ends removed

Method:

1. Wash the fruit and pat dry with the paper towels.
2. Peel and cut the kiwifruit, banana and watermelon into chunks.
3. Carefully thread one piece of each fruit onto a skewer.
4. Keep going until the fruit is used up.
5. Put some yoghurt in a small bowl.
6. Add a teaspoon of yoghurt onto the skewer and eat!

❶ Right there

(a) Circle yes or no.

   (i)   The fruit is washed.   YES   NO

   (ii) The grapes are cut into chunks.   YES   NO

   (iii) Metal skewers are used.   YES   NO

   (iv) Strawberry yoghurt is put in a bowl.   YES   NO

   (v) The grapes are green.   YES   NO

FRUITY SNACKS – 2

Use the text on page 23 to answer the questions.

❶ Right there

(b) Write the numbers 1 to 6 next to each sentence to show the order of how to make the fruity snacks.

☐ Keep going until the fruit is used up.

☐ Wash the fruit and pat dry with the paper towels.

☐ Add a teaspoon of yoghurt onto the skewer and eat!

☐ Peel and cut the kiwifruit, banana and watermelon into chunks.

☐ Put some yoghurt in a small bowl.

☐ Carefully thread one piece of each fruit onto a skewer.

❷ Think and search

(a) Colour the fruit on the skewer correctly.

(b) Why do you think green grapes were used and not red?

_____

_____

_____

❸ On my own

(a) Why is a blunt knife used?

_____

_____

_____

(b) Why are the sharp ends removed from the skewers?

_____

_____

_____

FRUITY SNACKS – 3

Would you change any of the ingredients if you wanted to make the fruity snacks?

❶ (a) Tick the fruits and the toppings you would like to choose from.

(b) Add two more you would like.

Fruits

strawberries ☐

grapes ☐

bananas ☐

kiwifruit ☐

watermelon ☐

peaches ☐

pineapple ☐

_____ ☐

_____ ☐

Toppings

strawberry yoghurt ☐

banana yoghurt ☐

passionfruit yoghurt ☐

cream ☐

chocolate topping ☐

_____ ☐

_____ ☐

❷ Write words to show how you would make the snacks.

Method

1. Wash the fruit and pat dry with the paper towels.

2. Cut the _____ into chunks.

3. Carefully thread one piece of each fruit onto a skewer.

4. Keep going until the fruit is used up.

5. Put some _____ in a small bowl.

6. Add a teaspoon of it onto the skewer and eat!

Teacher information

Genre:

Timetable

Question types and comprehension strategies:

- Analyses and extracts information from a timetable to answer literal, deductive and evaluative questions.
- Compares information from text with own written information.
- Scans text to locate information.

Worksheet information:

- If pupils are unfamiliar with the concept of a timetable, they would benefit from the opportunity to see how their school day is divided into blocks of time and to become aware of how their class timetable operates over at least one day.
- Pupils may need help to understand the time blocks given on Sarah's timetables.
- Recalling and recording the personal timetable on page 29 will be challenging for many pupils. A similar timetable could be sent home for the pupils to complete with parental assistance so that they have access to the required information.

Answers:

Pages 27–28

1. (a) (iii)   (b) (ii)
   (c) (i) No   (ii) Yes   (iii) Yes   (iv) No   (v) Yes
2–3. Teacher check

Page 29

1. Teacher check
2. Teacher check
3. Teacher check

Extension:

- Pupils formulate questions to ask each other about both Sarah's and their own individual timetables.
- Collect different types of timetables for pupils to practise reading. Discuss how they are set out and evaluate them in terms of how easy they are to understand; for example, bus, train and television timetables.

Sᴀʀᴀʜ's ᴛɪᴍᴇᴛᴀʙʟᴇ – 1

Read the timetable.

TIME	MONDAY	TUESDAY
3.30	home from school	home from school
	afternoon tea	afternoon tea
4.00	play with friends	get ready for music
		drive to music
4.30	play with friends	music lesson
5.00	watch TV	drive home
		shop with Mum
5.30	watch TV	watch TV
6.00	dinner	dinner
6.30	music practice	watch TV
7.00	shower and pyjamas	shower and pyjamas
7.30	reading or homework	reading or homework
8.00	clean teeth	clean teeth
	story in bed and sleep	story in bed and sleep

❶ Right there

Tick the correct ending to each sentence.

(a) On Monday, Sarah

    (i) goes to a music lesson. ☐

    (ii) shops with her mum. ☐

    (iii) has a shower at 7 o'clock. ☐

    (iv) has dinner at 5 o'clock. ☐

(b) Sarah plays with her friends

    (i) before her music lesson. ☐

    (ii) before she watches TV. ☐

    (iii) after dinner. ☐

    (iv) at 5 o'clock. ☐

Sᴀʀᴀʜ's ᴛɪᴍᴇᴛᴀʙʟᴇ – 2

Use the text on page 27 to answer the questions.

❶ Right there

(c) Tick yes or no after each sentence.

(i) Sarah watched more TV on Monday. 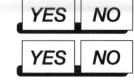 YES | NO

(ii) Dinner is at the same time on both days. YES | NO

(iii) Sarah puts on her pyjamas before she cleans her teeth. YES | NO

(iv) Sarah watched TV before her music lesson. YES | NO

(v) Sarah and her friends play before her music practice. YES | NO

❷ Think and search

(a) Why do you think Sarah is allowed to watch TV after dinner on Tuesday?

_____

_____

(b) Why doesn't Sarah do music practice on Tuesday?

_____

_____

❸ On my own

(a) Draw a picture to show the time in Sarah's day that you think is the best.

Sarah's Timetable – 3

1 Complete this timetable to show what you do after school.

Name:

_____

Day of the week:

_____

Time

Time	
3.30	
4.00	
4.30	
5.00	
5.30	
6.00	
6.30	
7.00	
7.30	

2 Read your timetable and answer the questions.

(a) What time did you have dinner?

_____

(b) Did you play with your friends?

_____

(c) Did you watch TV after dinner?

_____

(d) Did you go to bed after half past 7?

_____

3 Look at one day of Sarah's timetable on page 27 and compare it with yours.

(a) Who had dinner earlier?

_____

(b) Who spent more time watching TV?

_____

(c) Which timetable do you like better? Why?

_____

_____

Prim-Ed Publishing   www.prim-ed.com   Primary comprehension

THE CAMPING TRIP

Teacher information

Genre:

Letter

Question types and comprehension strategies:

- Analyses and extracts information from a letter to answer literal, deductive and evaluative questions.
- Compares information in a text to his/her own experience.
- Makes connections between events in a text and his/her own experience.

Worksheet information:

- A simple letter format is presented on page 31. Commas and full stops are not required at the end of the greeting or the conclusion and the paragraphs are separated by an obvious space.
- Pupils do not have to base their comparison on page 33 on a holiday they have actually had.

Answers:

Pages 31–32

1. (a) (i) Caris (ii) Aunty Kerry
   (b) sandwiches and hot chocolate
   (c) The letter was about a camping trip.
   (d) Mum gave Ryan a colouring book to stop him grizzling.
2. (a) walk in the woods, play with friends or play on the adventure playground
   (b) (i) Yes (ii) No (iii) Yes (iv) Yes
3. Teacher check

Page 33

Teacher check

Extension:

- Pupils may enjoy reading the following series of books:
  The jolly postman (or other people's letters) Janet and Allan Ahlberg
  The jolly pocket postman Janet and Allan Ahlberg
  The jolly Christmas postman Janet and Allan Ahlberg

THE CAMPING TRIP – 1

Read the letter.

Dear Aunty Kerry

I am writing to tell you about the camping trip we went on in the school holidays. Mum and Dad woke Ryan and me up at 6 o'clock in the morning. It was still dark! We ate our breakfast in the car while Dad drove. Mum had made sandwiches and a flask of hot chocolate.

It took three hours to drive to the campsite. I listened to music on my personal mp3 player. Ryan grizzled a lot as he was bored. Mum gave him a colouring book which kept him quiet for a while.

When we got there we helped unpack the car and set up the tent. Then we went exploring with Mum and Dad. Several other families were also staying there. One family had a girl my age and a boy Ryan's age. We played together a lot.

There was so much to do at the camp. We could swim, go canoeing or fish in the lake. Dad and Ryan caught a huge trout. They were very pleased! We also went walking in the woods, except Ryan had to be carried some of the way. At the campsite there was an adventure playground with a fort and a wobbly bridge.

We had a great time and I was sad to leave. Hope to see you soon.

Love Caris

❶ Right there

(a) Answer the questions.

   (i) Who wrote the letter?

   _____

   (ii) Who was the letter written to?

   _____

(b) Draw or write what the children had for breakfast in the car.

THE CAMPING TRIP – 2

Use the text on page 31 to answer the questions.

❶ Right there

(c) Underline the best answer.

    (i) The letter is about the school holidays.

    (ii) The letter is about a camping trip.

    (iii) The letter is about catching a fish.

(d) How did Mum stop Ryan from grizzling in the car?

_____

_____

❷ Think and search

(a) List two more things the children could do while on camp.

swim, go canoeing, fish,

_____

_____

(b) Answer yes or no.

    (i) The children made friends at the camp.   YES   NO

    (ii) Ryan was older than Caris.   YES   NO

    (iii) Ryan got tired on the walk.   YES   NO

    (iv) The children would have liked to stay longer.   YES   NO

❸ On my own

Draw and label what you would like to have done if you were at the campsite.

THE CAMPING TRIP – 3

1 Read about Caris's holiday below. Then think about a time you went on a camping trip or another kind of holiday, or imagine you have been on one. Complete the empty boxes with words or pictures about your trip.

		Caris	You
(a)	Where did she/you go?	a camping trip	
(b)	How did she/you get there?	by car	
(c)	When did she/you leave?	6 o'clock	
(d)	How long did it take to get there?	three hours	
(e)	What did she/you do on the way?	• ate breakfast • listened to music	
(f)	Where did she/you stay?	in a tent	
(g)	What did she/you do there?	• fished • went canoeing • swam • played with new friends • played on the adventure playground • went walking in the woods	

JOHNNY APPLESEED

Teacher information

Genre:

Folktale

Question types and comprehension strategies:

- Analyses and extracts information from a folktale to answer literal, deductive and evaluative questions.
- Makes comparisons between the past and the present by making connections using personal background knowledge and some information from the text.
- Creates visual images based on sensory imaging.

Worksheet information:

- Pupils will need to understand that folktales were generally passed on by word of mouth. Therefore, they changed and many became exaggerated. The less believable of these are called 'tall tales'.
- Discuss some of the differences between life in America 200 years ago and life today before pupils complete Question 2 on page 36
- With a partner, pupils could discuss some of the possible sights, sounds and smells Johnny might encounter, before imagining themselves in the situation outlined in Question 1 on page 37.
- Some pupils may require assistance to complete Question 2 on page 37.

Answers:

Page 35–36

1. (a) (i) Yes   (ii) No   (iii) Yes   (iv) Yes   (v) No
2. Teacher check
3. Teacher check

Page 37

1. Teacher check
2. Teacher check

Extension:

- Read and discuss other folktales about past heroes and where and when they lived; for example, Ned Kelly in Australia, Joan of Arc in France and King Arthur in Britain.
- Play Chinese Whispers to demonstrate to pupils how a simple story can be changed, unintentionally, by many retellings.

JOHNNY APPLESEED – 1

Read the folktale.

Johnny Chapman travelled around America about 200 years ago with a bag of apple seeds on his back. He sold small apple trees he had grown and gave seeds away to the settlers and the native Americans. They didn't know his name, so they called him Johnny Appleseed.

He was a kind, gentle man who wanted to plant apple trees so that no-one would ever be hungry. With his cooking pot on his head like a hat and without any shoes, he travelled alone, making friends with everyone. He was especially popular with the children and even became friends with some of the wild animals he came across.

There are many interesting stories told about him but they may not all be true.

One is about about a bear and its cubs sleeping inside a hollow tree trunk with Johnny one night during a snowstorm. They did not attack him and he left safely the next day.

Another story is about a rattlesnake that tried to bite him but couldn't get its fangs through his skin because it was 'as tough as an elephant's hide'.

Stories like these that people tell each other are often called 'tall tales'.

It is amazing that some of the trees Johnny Appleseed planted so long ago are still growing. Even today, people are eating and enjoying apples from these trees.

❶ Right there

(a) Write yes or no after each sentence.

(i) Children liked Johnny Appleseed.

(ii) Johnny Appleseed wore shoes.

(iii) He made friends with some wild animals.

(iv) The pot he wore on his head was for cooking.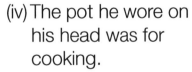

(v) All of the trees he planted have died.

Johnny Appleseed – 2

Use the text on page 35 to answer the questions.

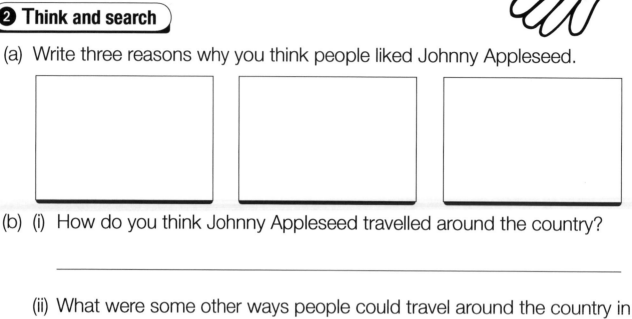

❷ Think and search

(a) Write three reasons why you think people liked Johnny Appleseed.

(b) (i) How do you think Johnny Appleseed travelled around the country?

_____

(ii) What were some other ways people could travel around the country in those days?

_____

❸ On my own

(a) (i) Which of the two tall tales about Johnny Appleseed do you think is more likely to be true?

_____

_____

(ii) Why do you think this?

_____

_____

_____

_____

_____

(b) Draw an apple tree, naming these parts:

branches   leaves   fruit
roots   trunk

JOHNNY APPLESEED – 3

1 Imagine you are Johnny Appleseed walking through the woods. Think about what you might see, hear and smell and draw the picture.

2 Johnny Appleseed lived 200 years ago. Think about the differences between then and now to complete the chart.

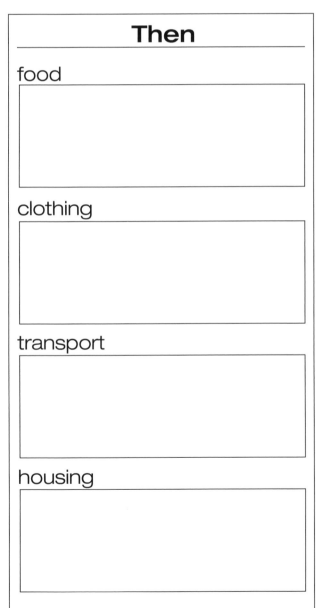

Then	Now
food	food
clothing	clothing
transport	transport
housing	housing

A VISIT FROM PLANET ZOG

Teacher information

Genre:

Science fiction

Question types and comprehension strategies:

- Analyses and extracts information from a science fiction narrative to answer literal, deductive and evaluative questions.
- Uses sensory imaging to complete an illustration.
- Makes predictions based on text, personal background and experience.

Worksheet information:

Pupils could work in pairs to complete page 41, particularly Question 2. Two pairs of pupils could role-play being the aliens and the two boys, before writing a conversation in the speech balloons.

Answers:

Pages 39–40

1. (a) (i) Planet Zog   (ii) by spaceship   (iii) Earthlings
   (iv) The boys were hiding behind some bushes.
   (b) (i) gasped   (ii) politely   (iii) strange
   (iv) peered
   (c) (i) False   (ii) False   (iii) True
   (iv) True
2. (a) The spaceship landing and taking off.
   (b) Teacher check
3. (a) Teacher check
   (b) Teacher check

Page 41

Teacher check

Extension:

- Books containing science fiction stories suitable for this age group are:

  There's no place like space: All about our solar system (Cat in the Hat's learning library) by Tish Rabe

  Jed and the space bandits by Jean and Claudio Marzollo

  Aliens for breakfast by Jonathan Etra and Stephanie Spinner

  Commander Toad in space by Jane Yolen

A VISIT FROM PLANET ZOG – 1

Read the science fiction story.

'Jake! Do you want to come to the park and play football?' yelled my older brother, Harry.

'Sure do!' I yelled back.

We raced over to the park and began to kick the ball. Harry kicked it so hard it went into the bushes. He came to help me find it.

Suddenly, we heard a strange whirring noise and a swoosh! Ducking down behind the bushes, we peered out. We gasped in surprise. A spaceship had just landed! It had 'Planet Zog' written on the side.

A little door opened and out hopped two aliens. They looked around and then hopped up to a tree. 'Hello, Earthling', said the aliens politely. The tree didn't say a word. They hopped up to a bin. 'Hello, Earthling', they said again. The bin didn't say a word. Next, they hopped up to a tap. 'Hello, Earthling', they said once more. The tap didn't say a word.

The aliens looked at each other. 'The earthlings have not learnt how to speak yet', one of them said. 'Let's come back another time.'

So, with a whirr and a swoosh they zoomed off into space.

❶ Right there

(a) Answer the questions.

    (i) Where did the aliens come from? _____

    (ii) How did they arrive on Earth? _____

    (iii) What did they call the 'people' on Earth? _____

    (iv) Why couldn't they see Jake and Harry? _____

_____

A VISIT FROM PLANET ZOG – 2

Use the text on page 39 to answer the questions.

❶ Right there

(b) Match each word in the story to its meaning.

    (i) took a sudden, quick breath of air •   • peered

    (ii) speaking with good manners   •   • gasped

    (iii) queer or odd   •   • politely

    (iv) looked from a hiding place   •   • strange

(c) Colour true or false.

    (i) Jake kicked the ball into the bushes.   **True** **False**

    (ii) There were three aliens.   **True** **False**

    (iii) The aliens moved by hopping.   **True** **False**

    (iv) The boys were playing football.   **True** **False**

❷ Think and search

(a) What made the strange whirring and swooshing noises?

_____

(b) Do you think the aliens were friendly? Explain your answer.

_____

_____

❸ On my own

(a) Why do you think the aliens thought the tree, bin and tap were people?

_____

_____

_____

(b) Draw something else in the park the aliens might have thought was an Earthling.

A VISIT FROM PLANET ZOG – 3

1 The picture of the aliens on page 39 does not show their faces. Close your eyes and imagine what their faces might look like. Draw their faces in the outlines below and colour them in.

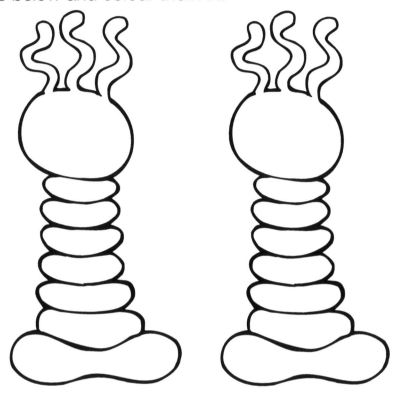

2 Imagine you are Jake. You and Harry have decided to come out from behind the bushes and talk to the aliens. Write what you think you would say to each other in the speech balloons.

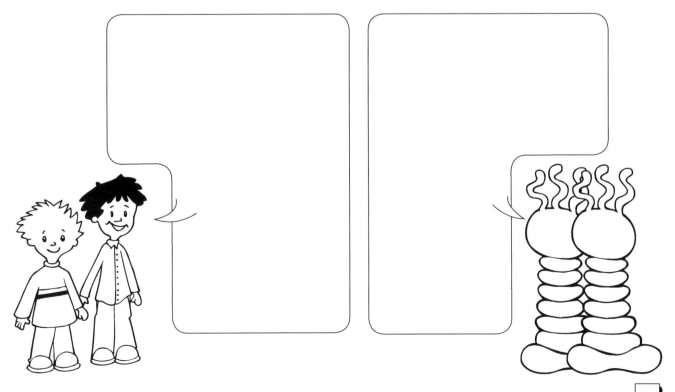

Teacher information

Genre:

Map

Question types and comprehension strategies:

- Analyses and extracts information from a map to answer literal, deductive and evaluative questions.
- Uses sensory imaging to appreciate the locations shown on the map.
- Makes connections between points on the map.

Worksheet information:

- When studying the map, discuss the use of pictorial images to represent specific things.
- Discuss the probability that most people living permanently on the island rely, in some way, on the chalet park for their work.

Answers:

Pages 43–44

1. (a) Holiday Island Tourist Chalet Park
   (b) pony trekking, canoeing, tennis
   (c) (i) False   (ii) True   (iii) False   (iv) True
2. Teacher check
3. Teacher check

Page 45

Teacher check

Extension:

- Pupils study other simple maps, and draw their own holiday island map.
- Read literature involving maps or create story maps from stories.

HOLIDAY ISLAND – 1

Study the map of Holiday Island.

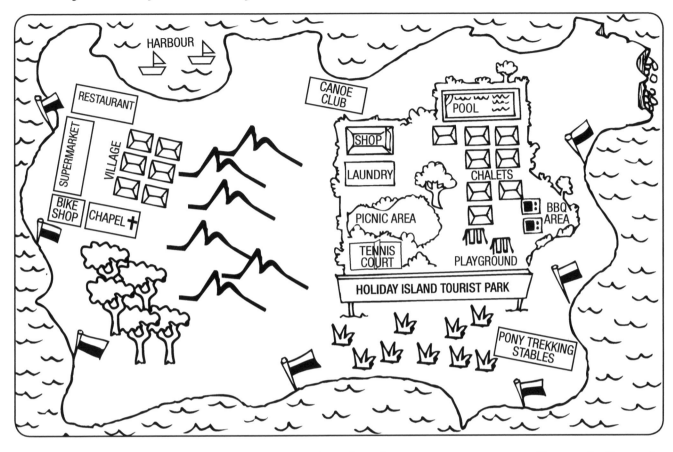

Tourists are taken by ferry to the island, where no cars are allowed. People cycle and walk everywhere, enjoying the fresh air and exercise.

❶ Right there

(a) Where do tourists stay on Holiday Island?

_____

(b) Circle the activities you can do on Holiday Island.

pony trekking	*go-kart racing*	*canoeing*	*tennis*	*bowling*

(c) Tick true or false.

    (i) The trees are next to the rocky cliffs .   *True* ☐   *False* ☐

    (ii) The village is close to the harbour .   *True* ☐   *False* ☐

    (iii) The hills are near the sea.   *True* ☐   *False* ☐

    (iv) There are many safe beaches for swimming .   *True* ☐   *False* ☐

HOLIDAY ISLAND – 2

Use the map on page 43 to answer the questions.

❷ Think and search

(a) Why is Holiday Island a great place to visit if you enjoy doing things outside?

_____

_____

(b) Name some places you could go through on a pony trek.

_____

(c) Write four jobs people who live in the village might have.

❸ On my own

(a) Draw pictures of you enjoying yourself doing two activities on the island. Label each picture.

(b) Why do you like these activities?

_____

_____

Holiday Island – 3

Use the map on page 43 to help you answer the questions.

1 It is your first day on Holiday Island. Explore and write about it below.

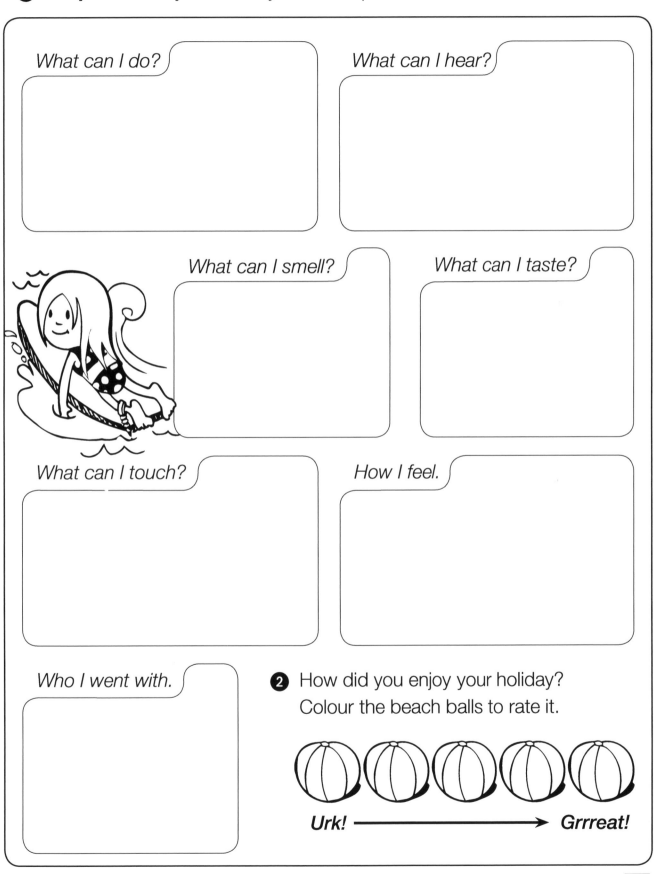

What can I do?

What can I hear?

What can I smell?

What can I taste?

What can I touch?

How I feel.

Who I went with.

2 How did you enjoy your holiday?
Colour the beach balls to rate it.

Urk! ⟶ Grrreat!

Genre:

Humour

Question types and comprehension strategies:

- Analyses and extracts information from a humorous story to answer literal, deductive and evaluative questions.
- Uses sensory imaging to answer questions about the humorous story.
- Summarises information to retell the story within a given framework.
- Scans text to seek specific information to provide answers.

Using the worksheets:

Read and discuss the text with the pupils. Highlight the two main events of the story. Explain that event one, Timothy in the enclosure, is detailed, including his attempted rescue by Mrs James and their fall from the tree. Details of the monkeys' adventure after their escape is left open for the pupils to suggest. On page 49, discuss possible scenes for each box. Ask relevant questions to help pupils with ideas; e.g. for box 2, 'How were the monkeys moving? What noises were they making? How do you think they were feeling?'

Answers:

Pages 47–48

1. (a) The baby monkey was holding a banana.

   (b) The baby monkey tickled Timothy under the arms.

   (c) A bright flash from a camera upset the monkeys.

2. (a) (i) False   (ii) True   (iii) False   (iv) True

3. Teacher check

Page 49

Teacher check

Extension:

- The planned stories from page 49 could be written in full.
- Pupils could research the dangers to themselves and the animals of entering an enclosure in the zoo without supervision.
- Research countries of origin of zoo animals.
- Make a collection of humorous stories involving animals.

MONKEY BUSINESS AT THE ZOO – 1

Read the humorous story.

'For the last time, calm down!' screeched Mrs James to her class as she tried to help Timothy down from the tree in the monkey enclosure.

'Why on earth did you get yourself into this mess?' she hissed at the frightened boy as a baby monkey fed him a banana.

Mrs James was just about to reach the trembling boy when the monkey decided to tickle him under the arms. Timothy let go of the branch he was holding and came tumbling down. As he fell, his hand caught in his teacher's hair and they fell together. Timothy's classmates howled with laughter.

By now, a zoo keeper had arrived to rescue the teacher and her pupil. A sudden bright flash from a camera upset two monkeys and they jumped on the keeper before she could shut the gate. In an instant, three cheeky monkeys hopped down from their branches and dashed down the path towards the children's playground.

1 Right there

(a) Tick the correct statement.

  (i) The baby monkey was wearing a hat. ☐

  (ii) The baby monkey was waving a flag. ☐

  (iii) The baby monkey was holding a banana. ☐

(b) What happened to make Timothy let go of the branch?

_____

(c) What made the monkeys jump on the zoo keeper?

_____

MONKEY BUSINESS AT THE ZOO – 2

Use the text on page 47 to answer the questions.

❷ Think and search

(a) Tick true or false.

(i) Timothy's classmates were miserable.   *True* ☐ *False* ☐

(ii) The monkeys were having a good day.   *True* ☐ *False* ☐

(iii) Timothy was an obedient boy.   *True* ☐ *False* ☐

(iv) Timothy was ticklish.   *True* ☐ *False* ☐

❸ On my own

(a) Imagine you are one of the characters from the story. Draw and write about the character below.

character: _____

What did your character …

feel? _____

see? _____

taste? _____

smell? _____

hear? _____

(b) What do you think the zoo keeper might have said to Mrs James when the panic was all over?

(c) Draw a face to show how each person enjoyed the day.

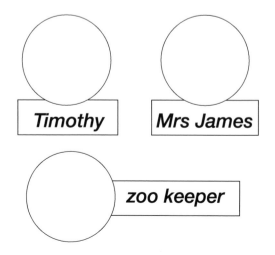

Timothy

Mrs James

zoo keeper

Monkey business at the zoo – 3

How strange it would have been to see three monkeys running down the path! What mischief do you think they may have made before being caught?

1 Use the boxes below to help write ideas and plan a story about the monkeys' adventure.

Title:

Running down the path.	At the playground.

Who joined in?	Who caught them? How were they captured?

How did the adventure end?

2 Use this plan to write a fun adventure story. Share it with a friend or the class.

O'LEARY'S LEPRECHAUN SHOW

Teacher information

Genre:

Poster

Question types and comprehension strategies:

- Analyses and extracts information from a poster to answer literal, deductive and evaluative questions.
- Uses sensory imaging to determine atmosphere of a performance.

Worksheet information:

When reading the poster, encourage pupils to feel the fun of the performance. Which acts would they particularly enjoy? Can they imagine attending and enjoying the show with their families?

Answers:

Pages 51–52

1. (a) O'Leary's Magnificent Leprechaun Show
   (b) six performances
   (c) a park
2. Teacher check
3. Teacher check

Page 53

Teacher check

Extension:

- Pupils make a collection of posters for local activities.
- Design posters for current school activities.
- Use a poster as a prompt to present a mini-topic on a chosen subject.

O'LEARY'S LEPRECHAUN SHOW – 1

Read the poster advertising the show.

O'Leary's Magnificent Leprechaun Show

Come and enjoy O'Leary's Magnificent
Leprechaun Show!

☆ singing

☆ music

☆ dancing

☆ magic tricks

☆ daring gymnastic feats

The world's one and only performing
leprechaun company.

Performances at Coolin Park at 3 pm and 7 pm

Friday 22 May to Sunday 24 May

**Bring your picnic rugs and
hampers**

Tickets available from:
Tourist office
57 High Street
Queenstown

Join in the fun for your chance to find the pot of gold at the end of the rainbow!

❶ Right there

(a) What is the name of the show?

_____

(b) How many performances will there be?   _____

(c) Tick the correct answer.

The shows are taking place in,

(i) a theatre ☐   (ii) a stadium ☐   (iii) a park ☐

O'LEARY'S LEPRECHAUN SHOW – 2

Use the text on page 51 to answer the questions.

❷ Think and search

(a) What clue is there on the poster to suggest that there is

   (i) no seating provided at the shows? _____

   _____

   (ii) no food to buy at the shows? _____

   _____

(b) What things might you do to join in with the fun of the show?

_____

_____

❸ On my own

(a) What do you think would be the good things and bad things about having a performance in a park?

Write your ideas for both in the boxes.

good things

bad things

O'LEARY'S LEPRECHAUN SHOW – 3

What fun, a leprechaun show is coming to town!

1 Who will go with you to the show?

2 Draw the leprechaun in his bright costume.

3 What do you think you will …

(a) hear? _____

_____

(b) see? _____

_____

(c) taste? _____

_____

4 Draw or write what you will put in your picnic hamper.

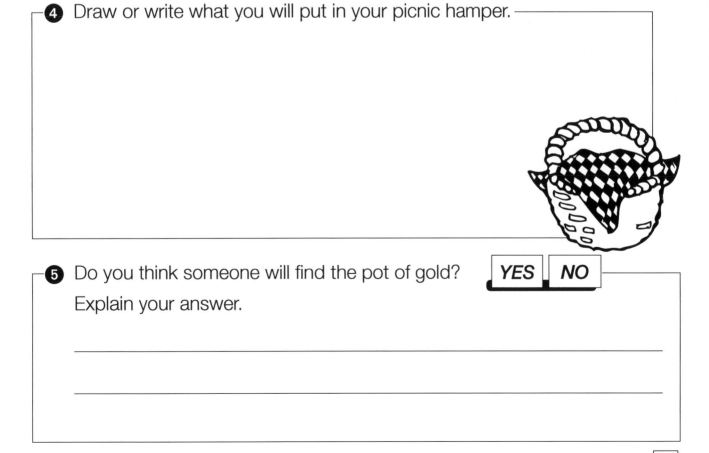

5 Do you think someone will find the pot of gold? **YES** | **NO**
Explain your answer.

_____

_____

A GIRL CALLED BREE

Teacher information

Genre:

Poetry

Question types and comprehension strategies:

- Analyses and extracts information from a limerick to answer literal, deductive and evaluative questions.
- Makes connections to choose appropriate rhyming words within the context of a limerick.
- Determines important information to illustrate what happened in a limerick.

Worksheet information:

- Pupils should be familiar with identifying rhyming words before completing the activity on page 57.
- A limerick is a nonsense poem made up of five lines with a special rhyming pattern. Lines 1, 2 and 5 rhyme and usually have the same number of syllables. Lines 3 and 4 rhyme and are shorter than the others.

Answers:

Pages 55–56

    1.   (a) (i) Bree   (ii) She only liked to watch TV.

                (iii) Her eyes became square.

                (iv) She got stuck to the chair.

        (b) square, chair

        (c) Bree, TV, free

        (d) five

2–3.   Teacher check

Page 57

    Teacher check

Extension:

- Books containing limericks and other nonsense poems suitable for this age group are:

  The mammoth book of jokes by Geoff Tibballs

  The Usborne book of jokes by Philip Hawthorn

  Rhymes, riddles and nonsense by Dr Seuss

  There's an awful lot of weirdos in our neighbourhood: A book of rather silly poems and pictures by Colin McNaughton

A GIRL CALLED BREE – 1

Read the limerick.

There once was a girl called Bree

Who would only watch the TV

Her eyes became square

And she stuck to the chair

And never again was she free

❶ Right there

(a) Answer the questions.

    (i) What was the girl's name? _____

    (ii) What did she like to do? _____

    _____

    (iii) What happened to her eyes? _____

    (iv) What did she get stuck to? _____

(b) Copy two words from the limerick that rhyme with 'bear'.

    (i) _____   (ii) _____

(c) Copy three words from the limerick that rhyme with 'sea'.

    (i) _____   (ii) _____

    (iii) _____

(d) How many lines are in the limerick?

| two | three | five | four | six |

A GIRL CALLED BREE – 2

Use the text on page 55 to answer the questions.

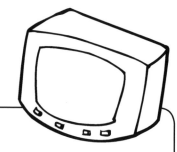

❷ Think and search

(a) Why do you think …

    (i) Bree's eyes became square? _____

    _____

    _____

    (ii) she stuck to the chair? _____

    _____

    _____

(b) Did the limerick have a happy ending? | YES | NO |

    Why? _____

    _____

❸ On my own

(a) What is your favourite TV programme?

_____

(b) Draw and label a picture about it.

_____

A GIRL CALLED BREE – 3

A limerick is a nonsense poem made up of five lines.
It rhymes in a special pattern.

> *There once was a girl called Bree*
>
> *Who would only watch the TV*
>
> *Her eyes became square*
>
> *And she stuck to the chair*
>
> *And never again was she free*

1 Underline in red the words that rhyme in lines 1, 2 and 5.

2 Underline in blue the words that rhyme in lines 3 and 4. These lines are shorter than the others.

3 Complete the limerick below, following the rhyming pattern.

> *There once was a clown from France*
>
> *Who wanted to learn how to* _____
>
> *He tripped over his toes*
>
> *And fell on his* _____
>
> *And got mud all over his* _____ *!*

4 Draw a picture of what happened to the clown.

CAPTAIN FISHHOOK AND THE BURIED TREASURE

Teacher information

Genre:

Book cover

Question types and comprehension strategies:

- Analyses and extracts information from a book cover to answer literal, deductive and evaluative questions.
- Scans for relevant information.
- Makes connections between a book cover viewed and one he/she creates.
- Makes predictions based on a visual text.

Worksheet information:

Pupils could view various book covers, discussing the cover illustration, blurb on the back cover, spine, title, author and illustrator, before completing the activity on page 61.

Answers:

Pages 59–60

1. (a) (i) *Captain Fishhook and the buried treasure*
   (ii) Ben Black   (iii) Molly Morgan
   (b) Teacher check
   (c) *Jolly rascal*
2. (a) The author writes the book.
   (b) The illustrator draws the illustrations (pictures) for the book.
3. Teacher check

Page 61

Teacher check

Extension:

- Pupils could view and discuss a variety of book covers, including fiction and nonfiction books, as well as comics, newspapers and magazines.
- Display covers of adult books and compare them with those designed for young children.
- Display pupils' favourite books and discuss whether the book cover played a part in their choices.

Look at and read the book cover.

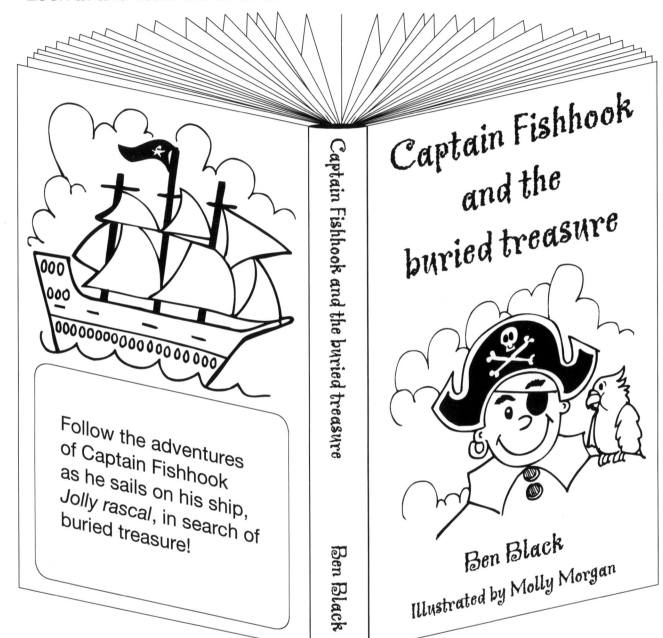

Captain Fishhook and the buried treasure

Ben Black

Captain Fishhook and the buried treasure

Ben Black

Illustrated by Molly Morgan

Follow the adventures of Captain Fishhook as he sails on his ship, *Jolly rascal*, in search of buried treasure!

❶ Right there

(a) Answer the questions.

   (i) What is the title of the book? _____

     _____

   (ii) Who is the author? _____

   (iii) Who is the illustrator? _____

CAPTAIN FISHHOOK AND THE BURIED TREASURE – 2

Use the text on page 59 to answer the questions.

❶ Right there

(b) Complete the sentence using some words from the book cover.

The book is about _____

_____

_____.

(c) What is the name of the ship? _____

❷ Think and search

(a) What does the author of a book do? _____

_____

(b) What does the illustrator of a book do? _____

_____

❸ On my own

(a) Think of other names for ...

   (i) the ship.

_____

_____

   (ii) the book.

_____

_____

_____

_____

(b) Draw and label where you think Captain Fishhook might find the buried treasure.

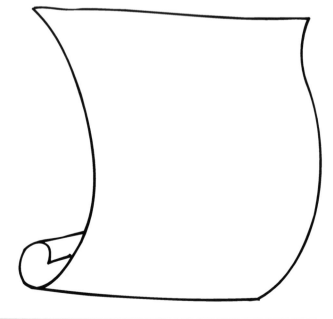

CAPTAIN FISHHOOK AND THE BURIED TREASURE – 3

1 Make a book cover of your own in the space below. It can be a story you have read or one you make up.

2 Write what will go on the back cover so a reader will know what the book is about.

_____

_____

_____

_____

THE HONEYBEE'S STING

Teacher information

Genre:

Myth

Question types and comprehension strategies:

- Analyses and extracts information from a myth to answer literal, deductive and evaluative questions.
- Uses synthesis to recall information and order details to sequence a story.

Worksheet information:

Pupils will need to complete Question 1 (a) before starting part (b) on page 65. The first five boxes require the pupils to write a sentence or draw a picture about events in the story. Once pupils have worked out the correct sequence of these they can then think of what might have happened next and draw and write a sentence in the blank box.

Answers:

Pages 63–64

1. (a) (i) Zeus   (ii) at the top of Mt Olympus
     (iii) a gold throne
(b) honeybee, deer, eagle, peacock
(c) (i) Zeus, wish   (ii) think   (iii) surprised
(d) (i) antlers   (ii) a beautiful colourful tail
     (iii) great wings   (iv) the power to give great pain
2. Teacher check
3. Teacher check

Page 65

Teacher check

Extension:

- Books containing myths suitable for this age group are:
Greek myths for young children by Heather Amery
15 Greek myth mini-books by Danielle Blood
Classic myths to read aloud by William F Russell

THE HONEYBEE'S STING – 1

Read the myth.

Long ago there was a king called Zeus. He lived at the top of Mt Olympus where he could see all his kingdom. One day, while he was sitting on his gold throne, he had an idea. Instead of just giving gifts to people, he decided to give them to the animals as well.

He called the animals to gather around his gold throne. 'Each of you will be granted one wish,' said the king, 'so think carefully'.

The eagle wished for great wings so she could soar high in the sky. The deer wished for antlers so he could use them against enemies. The peacock wished for a beautiful colourful tail. Then it was the honeybee's turn.

'What do you wish for, little honeybee?' asked the king.

'Only one wish will do', replied the honeybee. 'I wish to have the power to give any creature great pain whenever I choose.'

Zeus was surprised. 'What a horrible wish, but I must grant it', said the king. 'I will give you a sharp sting. However, you must only use it in times of anger or danger. And you will only be able to use it once, for using it will cost you your life.'

And to this day, the little honeybee dies after it stings another creature.

❶ Right there

(a) Answer the questions.

    (i) What was the king's name? _____

    (ii) Where did he live? _____

    (iii) What did he like to sit on? _____

(b) Circle the animals you read about in the story.

    honeybee   bear   deer   ant   eagle   peacock

THE HONEYBEE'S STING – 2

Use the text on page 63 to answer the questions.

❶ Right there

(c) Fill in the missing words.

| *think* | *wish* | *surprised* | *Zeus* |

(i) _____ granted each animal one _____.

(ii) He told the animals to _____ carefully.

(iii) Zeus was _____ when he heard the honeybee's wish.

(d) Join a line to what each animal wished for.

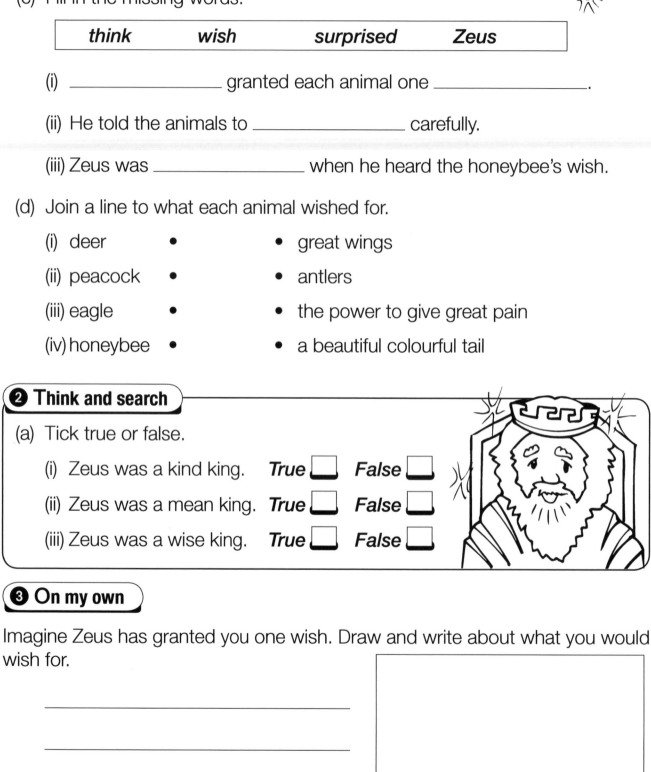

(i) deer •   • great wings

(ii) peacock •   • antlers

(iii) eagle •   • the power to give great pain

(iv) honeybee •   • a beautiful colourful tail

❷ Think and search

(a) Tick true or false.

(i) Zeus was a kind king.   *True* ☐   *False* ☐

(ii) Zeus was a mean king. *True* ☐   *False* ☐

(iii) Zeus was a wise king. *True* ☐   *False* ☐

❸ On my own

Imagine Zeus has granted you one wish. Draw and write about what you would wish for.

_____

_____

_____

_____

THE HONEYBEE'S STING – 3

Use the text on page 63 to answer the questions.

1 (a) Draw the missing pictures and write the missing sentences.

(b) In the last box, draw and write what you think will happen next.

(c) Colour and cut them out and put them in the correct order.

_____

The eagle wished for great wings
so she could soar high in the sky.

The honeybee wished for the power
to give any creature pain.

_____

_____

_____

Genre:

Horror story

Question types and comprehension strategies:

- Analyses and extracts information from a horror story to answer literal, deductive and evaluative questions.
- Predicts, based on prior knowledge and information provided in the text.
- Synthesises information to retell the story within a given framework.

Worksheet information:

- Before completing Question 3 on page 68, pupils will benefit from opportunities to discuss some of the things that may possibly have happened to the little brother and to understand that there is no correct answer because the writer has left the ending to the reader's imagination.
- The story framework on page 69 allows pupils to retell the story either briefly or in some detail. Pupils who want to write a longer story and need more space can rewrite each sentence beginning, as they write their retell, on a separate sheet of paper.

Answers:

Pages 67– 68

1. (a) (i) cup   (ii) book   (iii) on   (iv) eating
2. (a) (i) Yes   (ii) No   (iii) No   (iv) No   (v) Yes
3. Teacher check

Page 69

Teacher check

Extension:

- Brainstorm some of the comments Hannah's mother could have made when Hannah told her what had happened. These can be written on the board using speech marks.
- Read other stories about people or things being changed by magic, including:
  - *Cinderella*
  - *The frog prince*
  - *Rumplestiltskin*

THE MAGIC TRICK – 1

Read the horror story.

Hannah was reading an interesting book about magic. She read about lots of tricks you could play on your family and friends. There was one part all about making things disappear and another one about making things change.

Her mum had gone in next door for a cup of coffee with Mrs White and she had to look after her little brother again. He really was a noisy, messy little pest who just kept getting in the way and driving her nuts. He was playing some loud, boring computer game and yelling and shouting. She decided to try out one of the magic tricks.

On a piece of paper, she copied out the words of one of the magic spells and wrote her brother's name beside it. Next to it she drew a picture of a big fat snail. She held on to the paper and started to read out the words. It was very windy and before she had finished, the wind blew the paper away and she had to make up the last bit.

Her brother was very quiet and she wondered what trouble he was getting into this time. She went in to see but he wasn't in the computer room. 'Where is the little brat?' she asked herself as she walked around the house, but he was nowhere to be seen.

Hannah looked outside and noticed that there were a number of birds eating snails on the back lawn.

'Mum, Mum, Mum!' she screamed.

❶ Right there

(a) Write the missing words from the story.

   (i) Hannah's mother was having a _____ of coffee.

   (ii) The _____ was about magic tricks.

   (iii) Hannah wrote the magic words _____ a piece of paper.

   (iv) The birds were _____ snails.

THE MAGIC TRICK – 2

Use the text on page 67 to answer the questions.

② Think and search

(a) Write yes or no after each sentence.

(i) Hannah enjoyed reading. _____

(ii) All the words Hannah read out were written in the book. _____

(iii) Hannah wasn't worried about her little brother. _____

(iv) Her little brother was fun to look after. _____

(v) Hannah was frightened. _____

③ On my own

(a) What happened to Hannah's little brother? Draw a picture and write a sentence telling what you think really happened to him.

_____

_____

_____

THE MAGIC TRICK – 3

Use the story on page 67 to complete the activity.

1 Tell the story again in your own words. Your story can be long or short, but try to make it interesting.

Hannah was reading	Her mother
Her little brother was	She wrote magic words and she drew _____
Then she said the	She couldn't hear
So she went	Then Hannah noticed
The birds	Hannah yelled

THE PRINCESS AND THE PEA

Teacher information

Genre:

Fairytale

Question types and comprehension strategies:

- Analyses and extracts information from a fairytale to answer literal, deductive and evaluative questions.
- Makes predictions about specific characters.
- Synthesises information to comprehend and sequence events.

Worksheet information:

- Pupils should be familiar with the fairytale genre, particularly the 'once upon a time' and the 'and they all lived happily ever after' features.
- On page 72 they are asked to consider what living happily really means. Some discussion about what they predict would make the prince and the princess happy and what they think would ensure happy personal futures should precede this activity.
- The sequencing activity on page 73 may be challenging for some pupils. They may benefit from the opportunity of working with a partner.

Answers:

Pages 71–72

1. (a) (i) Yes   (ii) No   (iii) No   (iv) Yes   (v) Yes
2. Teacher check
3. Teacher check

Page 73

1. The sentences should be sequenced in this order:
   The prince goes travelling, looking for a princess.
   The prince comes home without a princess.
   The girl knocks on the castle door.
   The queen puts a pea in the bed.
   The girl wakes up after a bad night's sleep.
   The prince and princess get married.

2. Teacher check

Extension:

- Pupils dramatise particular scenes from the fairytale.
- Other fairytales involving princesses include:

  Sleeping Beauty   *Snow White*
  The twelve dancing princesses   *The frog prince*

- Pupils discuss similarities and differences between modern real-life and fairytale princesses.

THE PRINCESS AND THE PEA – 1

Read the fairytale.

Once upon a time there was a prince who wanted to marry a real princess. He travelled the world and met many girls who said they were princesses, but there was something about each one that wasn't quite right. He went home feeling very disappointed.

One evening there was a terrible storm. The wind was roaring and it was pouring with rain. The king heard knocking at the castle gates. He found a young girl there who said she was a princess and asked for his help. She didn't look like a princess. She had water dripping from her hair and down her clothes and her shoes were full of water. The king didn't believe her but he told her that she could stay for one night.

'We'll soon find out if she is a real princess', said the wise old queen.

She said nothing but she took everything off the bed and put a tiny pea on it. On top, she placed 20 mattresses and 20 eiderdowns.

The next morning, when they asked the girl how she had slept, she replied, 'Very badly. I don't know what it was, but I was lying on something hard and this morning I am black and blue'.

The prince and his family were very pleased. He took her for his wife and they all lived happily ever after.

❶ Right there

(a) Write **yes** or **no** after each sentence.

(i) The girl could feel the pea in her bed. _____

(ii) The queen told the king what she was going to do. _____

(iii) The girl had a good night's sleep. _____

(iv) This story has a happy ending. _____

(v) The prince went on a long trip, looking for a princess. _____

THE PRINCESS AND THE PEA – 2

Use the text on page 71 to answer the questions.

❷ Think and search

(a) Why didn't the king think the girl was a real princess?

_____

(b) Do you think the king was a kind man? | YES | NO |

Why? _____

_____

(c) Why didn't the queen tell anyone about the pea?

_____

(d) Why was the princess black and blue? _____

_____

❸ On my own

(a) Draw a picture of the princess and the prince living happily ever after.

(b) Draw some of the things that might make them happy.

Primary comprehension   Prim-Ed Publishing   www.prim-ed.com

THE PRINCESS AND THE PEA – 3

Use the text on page 71 to complete this activity.

1 Number the boxes to show the order of these events in the story.

The girl wakes up after a bad night's sleep. ....☐

The queen puts a pea in the bed. ....☐

The prince goes travelling, looking for a princess. ....☐

The prince and princess get married. ....☐

The girl knocks on the castle door. ....☐

The prince comes home without a princess. ....☐

2 Draw pictures to show the order in which things happened in the story.

1	2	3
4	**5**	**6**

STRANDED!

Teacher information

Genre:

Adventure

Question types and comprehension strategies:

- Analyses and extracts information from an adventure story to answer literal, deductive and evaluative questions.
- Scans text to seek specific information to provide answers.
- Uses synthesis to offer possible answers to divergent questions.

Using the worksheets:

- Explain any unfamiliar vocabulary.
- The activity on page 77 may be done orally before the pupils complete the page.

Answers:

Pages 75–76

1. (a) (i) False (ii) True (iii) False (iv) True

    (b) Sam waved his arms wildly above his head and shouted 'over here!'

2–3. Teacher check

Page 77

Teacher check

Extension:

- Answers to questions on page 77 could be stimulus for further writing.
- Arrange a visit from a lifeguard to discuss beach and swimming pool safety.
- Research shoreline wildlife.

STRANDED! – 1

Read the story.

Sam and Jess were digging a moat around their sandcastle. It had taken all morning to build and they were very proud of it. Sam stood up and watched the sea rushing in to fill the moat. It added the final touch to their masterpiece.

Jess stopped suddenly and cried, 'Sam, we're stranded! The sea has cut us off from the main beach! What shall we do?'

The friends looked at each other in dismay. They did not understand what had happened.

'My water bottle is empty', whispered Jess. Her eyes filled with tears. 'I can feel my skin prickling, too. I need some more sunscreen.'

'Don't worry, Jess, I'll look after you', comforted Sam.

He put his arm around his young friend. He had no idea what to do. Suddenly, a bright orange flash in the water caught his eye.

'Over here!' he shouted.

He ran to the water's edge, waving his arms wildly above his head. Within minutes, Sam and Jess were on board the life raft, enjoying their ride back to the main beach.

❶ Right there

(a) Tick true or false.

    (i) Sam and Jess were building a volcano.   **True** ⬚ **False** ⬚

    (ii) Jess had no water left.   **True** ⬚ **False** ⬚

    (iii) They were at the beach in the evening.   **True** ⬚ **False** ⬚

    (iv) The life raft was orange.   **True** ⬚ **False** ⬚

(b) What did Sam do to attract the attention of the lifesavers?

_____

STRANDED! – 2

Use the text on page 75 to answer the questions.

❷ Think and search

(a) Sam and Jess enjoyed their morning at the beach. Say why you think this statement is true.

_____

_____

_____

(b) How can you tell that Sam is a kind person?

_____

_____

(c) Which sentence in the story tells us that Jess was upset?

_____

(d) Who rescued Sam and Jess?

_____

❸ On my own

(a) Name three things to make playing on the beach safer.

- _____

  _____

- _____

  _____

- _____

  _____

(b) Use your list to draw a 'Safety at the beach' poster.

STRANDED! – 3

Use the text on page 75 to answer the questions.

1 Think about the questions in each box. What do you think the answers might be? There are no right or wrong answers.

(a) How old are Sam and Jess?

(b) Why are Sam and Jess at the beach together?

(c) Where are their parents?

(d) Why did they build their sandcastle away from the main beach?

(e) Who was waiting for Sam and Jess back at the main beach?

(f) What was said to Sam and Jess about their adventure?

THE POLAR BEAR

Teacher information

Genre:

Report

Question types and comprehension strategies:

- Analyses and extracts information from a report to answer literal, deductive and evaluative questions.
- Scans text to determine important information.
- Summarises text by recording keywords and phrases.

Worksheet information:

Pupils could use different colours to highlight keywords and phrases needed to complete the chart on page 81. The activity is suitable for working in pairs.

Answers:

Pages 79–80

1. (a) (i) North   (ii) thick, hair   (iii) four, sharp, paws
   (b) The polar bear has lots of little bumps on the bottom of its paws to help it grip the ice.
   (c) (i) True   (ii) False   (iii) False
       (iv) True   (v) False
2. (a) cub
   (b) Teacher check
3. (a) eagle, tiger, lion
   (b) Teacher check

Page 81

Teacher check

Extension:

- Pupils may enjoy reading books about animal facts from the following series, before writing a simple report for others to read.

  Animal books for young children published by Acorn Naturalists

  The faces of nature series by Mymi Doinet

  Wild, wild world series by Tanya Lee Stone

THE POLAR BEAR – 1

Read the report.

The polar bear is the largest bear in the world. It lives along the shores, on the ice and in the icy cold Arctic Ocean near the North Pole.

The polar bear has a very thick, white coat of hair that helps to keep it warm. It walks on four strong legs and has sharp claws on its very large paws. The paws have lots of little bumps on the bottom to help them grip on the ice. The polar bear has sharp teeth to help it eat its food.

This animal is usually found living alone. But a polar bear cub will live with its mother for about two and a half years. She protects it and teaches it how to hunt for food.

The polar bear hunts seals as its main food. It finds a seal's breathing hole in the ice. When the seal comes to the surface for a breath of air, the polar bear uses its huge paws and sharp claws to flip the seal up onto the ice.

A polar bear in the wild can live for about 20 years. One polar bear in a zoo lived for 41 years!

❶ Right there

(a) Write words from the report to finish the sentences.

(i) The polar bear lives near the _____ Pole.

(ii) It has a very _____, white coat of _____.

(iii) The polar bear has _____ strong legs,

_____ claws and very large _____.

(b) What does the polar bear have on its paws to help it grip on the ice?

_____

_____

THE POLAR BEAR – 2

Use the text on page 79 to answer the questions.

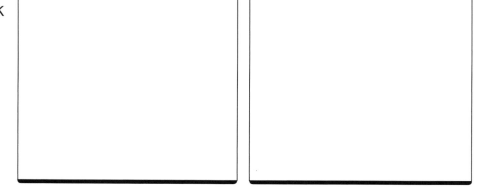

❶ Right there

(c) Answer true or false.

(i) The polar bear is the largest bear in the world. _____

(ii) It lives in a warm place. _____

(iii) It usually lives in a group. _____

(iv) It can live for about 20 years in the wild. _____

(v) Its favourite food is fish. _____

❷ Think and search

(a) What is the name of a young polar bear? _____

(b) Do you think a mother polar bear is kind? | YES | NO |

Why?_____

_____

❸ On my own

(a) Colour the animals that have sharp claws like the polar bear.

| spider | eagle | tiger | mouse | elephant | lion |

(b) Draw and label two animals that have a very thick coat of hair like the polar bear.

THE POLAR BEAR – 3

Use the text on page 79 to answer the questions.

1 Write words and phrases from the report about the polar bear to complete the chart.

The polar bear

Where does it live?

What does it look like?

coat ...

legs ...

claws ...

teeth ...

paws ...

What does it eat?

Interesting fact

Draw a polar bear near the breathing hole.